CHILDREN OF THE RESISTANCE

Children
of the Resistance

by LORE COWAN

HAWTHORN BOOKS, INC. PUBLISHERS   NEW YORK

940.54

To Ann and Davis Factor
in Gratitude for Their Generosity
during World War Two
to Those Who Were in Need

PREFACE

LET ME begin with the last words spoken by Edith Cavell on the twelfth of October, 1915, during World War One, before she was executed by the Germans: "I must have no hatred or bitterness toward anyone."

This book is not written with hatred, even though the grim, incredible background to all the stories is the Nazi occupation of various European countries during World War Two.

Many of my young friends, fortunately nurtured in freedom and independence, have often said to me, "We hear a great deal about the Resistance Groups and the Underground in the countries occupied by the Nazis, but what about the young people like ourselves? Didn't they do anything? Didn't they fight?"

By "young people," they mean teen-age children like themselves, not young men and women like the Scholls of the University of Munich, or the Israeli heroine Hannah Senesch, past their teens, whose fight against tyranny has become legendary, and who were murdered by the Nazis.

I have attempted to show in these stories that not all the "Young People" in Europe climbed on Hitler's Bandwagon. Far from it. In all the occupied countries, and in Germany itself, there were children who longed for freedom, who fought for it, and who died for it.

Research in the various countries has not been easy. A quarter of a century, more or less, has in many cases obliterated names and places.

Although these stories of what children did in their fight against Hitler are in one sense truly documentary, there is an element of fiction in the names of the heroic youngsters, and sometimes of where the events took place. Many of these people, who underwent great privation and suffering, are scattered over the globe. Some are dead, others prefer to forget the past, or to talk of their onetime comrades, and not of themselves.

"It's so long ago," is the frequent response to my questions. "Why dig it up?"

My answer to that is that the youth of today want to know, and need to be constantly reminded that freedom is precious, and that it is something that must, if necessary, be fought for, and that, in that fight for freedom throughout World War Two, the children of the Resistance played a noble and significant part.

They will always be an example to the young people of today.

My thanks are due to all those people, who wish to remain anonymous, for their patience and their kindly help, and to the Wiener Library for providing me with important guide lines and valuable sources.

CONTENTS

CHILDREN OF THE RESISTANCE

POOR PIERRE

OCTOBER, 1940. The Germans were masters of Norway, Denmark, Holland, Belgium, little Luxemburg, and much of France.

But they had lost the Battle of Britain, and to no people had this failure brought more silent joy than to the inhabitants of Pierre's village. For a time they practiced a "dumb insolence" that even the Nazis could not punish. Every time they passed a German in uniform, they solemnly looked up into the sky.

Owing to its strategic situation, Pierre's little village in Normandy had suffered out of all proportion to its three hundred inhabitants. It had to pay dearly for being near the coast, near rivers, near a canal, and at no great distance from Caen, the chief town of the Calvados, with its maze of roads and railways.

The German occupation of the village had robbed it of its *joie de vivre*. People had always enjoyed laughing in this small attractive place. Now freedom was dead. The days were glum, and nights, with their curfews, were grim.

An oppressive calm shrouded the main street as the day began. Only the explosive motorcycles of the German soldiers, as they raced through the village, punctured the silence. Henri Duplay, the much-loved and respected schoolmaster, who had served the village for forty years, plodded his weary way up the narrow, sloping street to his dilapidated school, nestling uncomfortably against the ancient church. Both had suffered from bombardment.

Duplay's reverie was broken by the "good morning" of his old friend, Monsieur Renaud, the pharmacist. The butcher, Paul Marcellin, was taking the shutters down, and paused to shrug his shoulders, as much as to say, "I don't know why I'm doing this. I've nothing to sell." Only outside the bakery was there a patient but worried line. Bread was rationed, but, who knows, there might be nothing left for a latecomer, or even for someone in the line.

The schoolmaster was now in sight of his gray, shabby school. He and the priest had pleaded with the German commandant for repairs to be carried out.

The priest pointed out that the church had a thirteenth-century nave in pure Norman-Gothic style. The commandant had roared with coarse laughter. He didn't give a damn if nobody ever went into the church again, and if it crumbled to pieces, thirteenth-century nave and all.

As for the school, if he had his way, he would put every boy and girl on a farm or in a factory, instead of stuffing them with useless knowledge. The schoolmaster and the priest never complained again, but they never forgot.

As he turned into the tiny playground, Henri Duplay wondered whether he wouldn't be wiser to disappear, and join General de Gaulle in London. True he was gray-haired and a bit bent, but he could still be very useful.

Yet, what would become of his senior class, of *"mes enfants,"* as he called them? Mlle. Martin, a tired spinster of fifty-five, had all her work cut out to look after the juniors. Too often he had to give her a helping hand. And what would his comrades in the Resistance think—they, who depended so much on his judgment and on his decisions? It would certainly look like desertion.

Surely the *Bon Dieu* would one day tire of these Nazi swine, and hand France back to her rightful owners, who would have to be worthy of such a trust.

As he entered the classroom, and the children rose respectfully, he could be heard murmuring to himself: *"L'avenir, c'est à moi."* (The future belongs to me.)

"Bonjour, maître," chorused the class.

"Bonjour, mes enfants."

School was over for the day. The children trooped out of the gate in twos and threes. They, too, had lost the fun and the high spirits that rightly belong to schoolchildren. They had learned to hate.

Only one boy, Pierre Labiche, was alone, and he was the time-honored butt of four of his schoolfellows, led by Jacques Fournier, the bully of the class.

> "Pierre is an idiot, Pierre is a fool,
> Pierre is the biggest dunce we have in the school."

The taunting shouts made no impression on Pierre, for the simple reason that the boy was stone deaf. In addition to being deaf, Pierre was also dumb. He had been so from birth, and it was not without reason that whenever the villagers spoke of him it was always "Poor Pierre."

Even those villagers who liked him and sympathized with him—and there were many—even they could think of no more kindly word than "plain" when they described how he looked. He was Nature's misfit, yet he had two redeeming features, large luminous eyes, and a charming smile that almost made him attractive.

Pierre's mother was dead. His father, an army reservist, had been called up, and had been killed in the Maginot Line. His only relative, with whom he lived, was Great-Aunt Paulette, his father's aunt.

Tired of getting no response from Pierre, and having vented some of their hatred in this useless manner, the bully and his cronies gave up with a last defiant shout. Not one of them dared do more than this, for Pierre, though only thirteen, had the strength of a young ox, and could have easily taken on any two or three of the boys.

The last shout brought Monsieur Renaud, the pharmacist, to the door of his store. It was almost a daily cue, and Pierre broke his solitary journey to shake hands with the pharmacist, who gently drew the boy into the store. He gave him a small bag of peppermint tea for Aunt Paulette, and then scribbled a few words on a strip of paper which he showed to Pierre—"Tonight, 1:30." The boy acknowledged receipt of the message by nodding, and the pharmacist lit the strip to finish the stump of a cigarette.

Aunt Paulette's cottage was a mile outside the village, and within sight of the sea. It was an old tumbledown building, always in need of repair, but it was home to Pierre and his aunt. Although they had no luxuries, they managed to scrape a living from the old orchard, and from the "cabbage patch," sometimes finding that a few potatoes could be exchanged for a little rare and delicious Normandy butter.

Everything Aunt Paulette produced was controlled by the German Command, but many a villager had cause to say "Thank you, Aunt Paulette."

"What the eye doesn't see," the old woman would say, "the heart doesn't grieve over, and in any case, if I had my way, I would sooner let the food rot than give it to the Nazis."

Her one consuming hate was for the Germans. In three wars—two in her own lifetime—they had killed all the men of her family, and this hatred was shared by Pierre, with whom she had learned to communicate by sign language.

When Pierre gave his aunt the pharmacist's message, all she replied was, "Be careful, Pierre, you are now the only man in the family, and our family must live on—for France."

The night was dark, a war night with not a glimmer of light. Pierre could hardly remember a night so pitch-black. From the window of his bedroom he scanned the sky, but could see nothing, even with his "X-ray eyes," as the schoolmaster called them. For Nature, who had deprived him of sound and speech, had compensated him with wonderful sight, with an unerring instinct for direction, and with a talent for ferreting things out in wood or forest.

As the old clock in the kitchen softly chimed the half hour, Aunt Paulette came into Pierre's room, to watch with him. She could hear the distant sound of plane engines, and she pointed the direction to Pierre. Then came the shattering fire of antiaircraft guns. They were firing blindly, for nothing was visible in the sky, and the searchlights could not pierce the dense cloud.

Pierre followed the searchlights, and in a split second he caught sight of what he thought was a parachute. Seconds passed, and the searchlights weaved their patterns, but there was no further sign of a parachute. Had he been mistaken? Aunt Paulette asked what he had seen. Had it been a parachute? Both of them knew what the penalty would be if he were caught breaking the curfew, particularly during an air raid.

And yet what if it had been an Allied airman? Instinctively Pierre felt that he was right about the parachute, and instinctively, too, he guessed that it would have come down in the woods. He had better get there before the Germans and their dogs made a search.

Pierre put on a pair of rubber-soled shoes, hugged his Aunt, and silently slipped out of the cottage.

Flying Officer Tracy was working as quickly, and as quietly as possible, to bury his parachute. Elmer Tracy, a twenty-three-year-old American, had joined the Royal Air Force, even though his country was not at war with the Nazis. He believed passionately in freedom, and was willing to die for it. This night his squadron had been detailed to protect bombers, who were to drop their load on a new subterranean airfield, about which the Underground in Pierre's village had relayed information.

His plane had been hit by a stray shell, and his only chance was to bail out. He landed in a small clearing in this wood, without any damage to himself, and now he was trying to bury the parachute.

Suddenly he froze. He had heard what he thought was a sound, a footstep on dry leaves. He waited tensely for the next move. If it were one German he might stand a good chance of killing him. Obviously there were no dogs, or they would have barked. If there were more than one, the chances would be against him. He could kiss the war good-bye. Tracy moved quietly and swiftly to the cover of a broad oak tree, and waited. Not a sound. Had he been mistaken? He could hear his heart thumping as the seconds ticked away.

He looked at the luminous dial of his wristwatch. Was it a second or a minute? Unable to restrain his curiosity any longer, he took out a pencil-thin flashlight, having first taken the safety catch off his revolver, and shielding the flashlight carefully, he pressed the button for a second. The pinpoint of light pierced the pitch-black night to reveal Pierre, about five yards away, standing motionless, with his fingers to his lips, enjoining silence.

An involuntary gasp escaped Flying Officer Tracy. "Jeez a kid."

Pierre moved swiftly forward, and with the help of a jack knife, ripping and cutting as fast as he could, they soon buried the remains of the parachute.

"Who are you?" whispered Tracy. There was no response. He asked the same question in his quite passable French, but still drew no answer. Perhaps, thought Tracy, the kid is right. It is dangerous even to whisper.

Hurriedly, with practically no sound, Pierre covered the place with leaves and fallen branches, then taking the officer by the hand he zigzagged his way through the wood. They had just reached a corner of Perrichon's farm, when the dogs began to howl. Pierre lay flat in a ditch, and pulled Tracy down beside him.

An owl hooted. Tracy shivered. The only welcome sound was the thump of bombs falling some miles away. At least some of the bombers had reached the target. They lay there for about sixty seconds, but to Tracy it seemed like an eternity. Was he right to trust this kid who refused to open his mouth? He knew the Nazis were offering big rewards for information about Allied airmen. Should he kill this boy, bury the body, and take a chance of escaping? At worst, he could only be sent to a prisoner-of-war camp. Anyway, as an American, with whose country Germany was not at war, there was little likelihood that the Gestapo would torture him. What was the best thing to do? Should he, at the point of a gun, make this boy confess?

At this moment a tug of the hand by Pierre broke Tracy's reverie, and, copying the boy, he wriggled along on all fours in the shadow of a thick hedge.

After five uncomfortable minutes, Pierre suddenly stopped. Peering into the darkness of a long road on the left, he had spotted a distant glimmer of light. Once again he put his fingers to his lips, and motioned Tracy to lie beside him.

The officer made one more attempt to communicate with the boy.

"*Je suis un officier Américain,*" he hissed. "*Parlez à moi. Dites-moi votre nom.*"

The boy's silence so annoyed him that he almost exploded.

"For Christ's sake, can't you answer a civil question? Are you a friend or an enemy?" In his anger he shook Pierre, but all he got was the same sign for silence.

Suddenly, night was turned into day, as a searchlight on a car swept the road and the surrounding countryside. The car halted within fifty yards of Tracy and Pierre, and the voices of two Germans carried clearly in the still night.

"I don't believe there was a parachute landing. The plane exploded, and the damned Englishman exploded with it."

"If there was a parachute landing," answered the other, "it would have been in the wooded hills, or much nearer Caen."

"Thank goodness that's outside our province. I don't like the idea of meeting a hand grenade or a knife in the back."

"These cursed Frenchmen, even in a small village like this, they never know when they are beaten. Between ourselves, these Resistance swine worry me. They don't care if they live or die as long as they kill us. Put one of them against a wall to shoot him and he shouts *Liberté, Egalité, Fraternité*. It makes me shiver."

"Let's go back to HQ. These ghostly shadows among the trees give me the creeps. We've done enough searching for one night. I can do with a glass of Calvados."

"Let's go. At least these French can make good schnapps."

Off went the car as though pursued by the devil himself.

Flying Officer Tracy took a deep, thankful breath. If this French lad had been in league with the Nazis, he could have given him away with the greatest of ease. He shook Pierre's hand, and whispered, *"Merci."* Pierre's smile was an adequate reply, as he took Tracy's hand, and once again they crawled on their knees in the shadow of the hedge.

Suddenly Pierre halted. He motioned Tracy to lie down, put his finger on the luminous dial of the officer's wristwatch, held up two fingers, and vanished.

What could the boy mean? Two hours? Two minutes? Would he be bringing two friends along? Within a minute Tracy heard a sound that he guessed was pebbles being thrown against a window.

Two minutes later Flying Officer Tracy was in the woodshed of Aunt Paulette's cottage. The small, wizened old woman was on her hands and knees, betraying a remarkable strength as she moved logs, scraped earth away, and shifted planks to uncover a hole, showing steps leading to a cellar.

Pierre bolted and barred the door of the shed, as his aunt descended, followed by Tracy. They reached a cell, little more than a hole in the ground. It contained a camp bed, and very little else in the way of conveniences.

"Do you speak French?" asked the old woman.

"A little," answered Tracy, "but I understand quite a lot."

"Good. I apologize for this hole, but this is your home until we can return you to England, which I hope will be soon."

"The boy who found me—"

"He is my nephew Pierre. He is deaf and dumb, not bad assets in these days. We communicate by sign language."

"Please apologize to him for me. I lost my temper with him, because he was silent. But isn't he too young for this sort—"

"Nobody is too young to fight for freedom," interrupted the old woman angrily. "What is life worth, even a young life, without freedom?"

There was a change of tone from the aunt, as she returned to more practical matters.

"You will exchange your uniform for this old suit. We will destroy your uniform. It is a pity, but it must be."

"Madame, I am an American who is fighting with the British. Do you understand my French, Madame?"

"Well enough."

"I know what you will have to suffer if I am caught here," continued Tracy, in his halting French. "Not only you, but that brave boy as well. Would it not be better if I went out into the night? After all, as an American—"

"Enough," hissed the old woman. "You are my guest and you will do as I say. As you can guess, you are not the first Allied fighter whom we have rescued. Obey my orders, ask no questions, and put your trust in God, and in the men of our Resistance. And now have a good drink of our Calvados"—she pointed to a bottle and a glass. "You are now in the Calvados country. It will help you to sleep. Tomorrow morning we will talk again. Good night."

The class had assembled for morning school. A buzz of excited speculation swept the class. For the first time that any pupil could remember, the schoolmaster was not there right on time. Had he been taken away during the night? It was not uncommon for a villager, without any warning, to be taken from his home, and to disappear for good. While the children speculated about their teacher, Pierre was gripped in an icy terror. For he alone knew that his schoolmaster would have been out on duty during the night with other members of the Resistance.

Pierre had no fear that the Gestapo would break the schoolmaster, but how much torture could that slender frame take? He consoled himself with the fact that when he reported this morning to Monsieur Renaud about the American airman, the pharmacist had said nothing about the schoolmaster.

Six minutes past his usual time, Monsieur Duplay entered the class.

"I am sorry, children, that I am late, but I, like many of you, had a very disturbed night."

A smile flashed between Pierre and his teacher. Pierre knew that he and the pharmacist had met to prepare a plan for the future.

"This morning we will talk about a heroine of France, a local girl we may rightly call her, for she was born in the Calvados." On the board the schoolmaster wrote CHARLOTTE CORDAY, 1768–1793. Underneath he wrote, *"Elle nous apprend à mourir"* ("She teaches us how to die.")

Barely had the words gone on the board when, without any ceremony, the door burst open, and in strode a German officer, followed by two subordinates. That it was not just a courtesy visit was evident from the fact that the officer was an Obersturmbannführer, an extremely high rank.

"Stand, children." The teacher saw no point in antagonizing the German.

"Heil Hitler!" shrieked the officer as he threw up his arm.

"Heil Hitler!" murmured the children. They were ordered by the officer to sit.

"I hope that I am not interrupting anything important," began the sarcastic Nazi, and then his cruel, hard eyes caught sight of the blackboard.

"What is this rubbish that you are teaching the children?"

"In the history of France—"

"You have no history, you old fool," shouted the German. "The only history you will have will be the history we, the Master Race, will write for you. Wipe that blasphemy off the board."

The teacher obeyed.

The German now displayed unusual charm as he spoke to the children.

"Some of you may have been awakened last night by antiaircraft fire. Naturally we drove off those foolish enemy airmen, and destroyed most of their planes over the sea. But we believe that one airman may have parachuted down, and that he may be in the neighborhood. We have decided to give a reward of fifty thousand francs and a special medal to any boy or girl who gives us information that may lead to the capture of this enemy airman. That is a wonderful reward, isn't it?"

There was silence.

"Answer me when I ask a question," stormed the officer.

"Yes, sir," came the obedient chorus.

"Also, one of my officers believes that he saw a boy enter the woods last night. He's not sure, because it was so dark."

This was a shot in the dark that the German thought worth trying.

"Now, I know that you are a very intelligent class," purred the Nazi. "Suppose you had to choose one of this class as the boy who broke the curfew—and remember it could be worth fifty thousand francs—who would you say that boy might be?"

There was a deathly silence as Jacques Fournier, the bully of the class, put up his hand.

"Yes, boy, who would you choose?"

"I would pick Pierre Labiche," came the prompt reply.

An audible gasp of astonishment came from the class.

"And why would you pick Pierre Labiche?" cooed the officer.

"Because he was eating chocolate this morning, and it must have been English chocolate, the way he enjoyed it."

"I can explain that—" interrupted the schoolmaster.

"You speak when you're spoken to," stormed the Nazi. Turning to the boy, he continued in a kindly seductive voice.

"You are a very intelligent boy, and very cooperative. What is your name?"

"Jacques Fournier, sir."

"Is your father Monsieur Fournier, the grain merchant?"

"Yes, sir," came the proud answer.

"He is a very sensible, cooperative man. He knows what is good for him. And now, will Pierre Labiche come out here."

Pierre had been following all this without hearing a word that had been spoken. He guessed that something was wrong, but he was surprised when the schoolmaster beckoned him to come from his seat, and to stand in front of the Obersturmbannführer.

"What is your name?" asked the officer.

No response.

"Answer when I speak to you, you impudent louse," and with his leather gloves he slashed Pierre across the face.

The boy did not blink, which infuriated the German.

"May I—" began the schoolmaster.

"Keep your mouth shut, you senile idiot. The boy is old enough to speak for himself."

Turning to Pierre, he repeated his question, only to be met with the same silence.

"You obstinate pig," and the leather gloves slashed the other side of Pierre's face, leaving red weals on both sides.

This was too much for twelve-year-old Gabrielle, the pharmacist's daughter. Tears were in her eyes as she jumped up and almost shrieked, "Please, sir, Pierre is deaf and dumb."

"Why didn't you say so?" asked the Nazi, but the schoolmaster was wise enough not to answer, as the inevitable question came— "How do you communicate with him?"

"By deaf-and-dumb sign language."

"Then ask him where he was last night."

Rapidly Pierre read the schoolmaster's message.

"Tell me that you were at home last night fast asleep, and that the chocolate you ate this morning I had given you yesterday. Begin."

As Pierre replied by signs, the teacher translated, "I was at home from the moment I left school yesterday, until I left home this morning."

"Ask him where he got the chocolate."

The schoolmaster did so. Before Pierre could answer, the officer shouted, "Stop. Tell him to write the answer on the blackboard."

Obeying his teacher's instructions, Pierre scrawled on the board, "Teacher gave me a piece yesterday."

The schoolmaster opened his desk and took out a moldy piece of chocolate.

"You will remember, sir, that we were given chocolate to distribute to the children when you occupied the village. I would stake my life that Pierre—Poor Pierre everybody calls him—could do nothing wrong. He is looked upon as the village idiot."

The Nazi paid little attention to the schoolmaster or to Pierre.

"Listen carefully, children." And turning to the teacher he said, "and write this down for this dumb idiot—just as there are rewards for your cooperation, so are there punishments for any disobedience, and for any illegal act against our army of occupation.

"For example, if one of you were to help any enemy airman who had been shot down, and be sure we would find out, you and your family would be sent to a concentration camp forever. Before then, however, you and your family would tell us all you know, because when your toenails are pulled out, and red-hot needles are put under your fingernails, you talk quickly enough. So tell this to your parents, and also tell them of the reward of fifty thousand francs. Heil Hitler!"

The children rose as he strode out, followed by his two subordinates.

There was a murmur in the class as the teacher turned to Jacques Fournier.

"And now, Jacques, why did you accuse Pierre?"

"It was only a joke, sir, because he wouldn't give me a piece of his chocolate this morning."

Spontaneously there came a storm of booing from everybody in the class.

"I'll leave you to the tender mercies of your schoolfellows. And now let us resume work. Write an essay on 'How I would spend fifty thousand francs.' "

The schoolmaster then "conversed" with Pierre.

"Have you anything to tell me?"

"Aunt Paulette is happy when a visitor comes."

"I know, but we must be very careful. They will watch us closely. The Nazi officer was not entirely satisfied. You were careless with the chocolate. It should never have come out of your home. It was lucky I had an old piece in my desk. Don't let it happen again. On such little things our lives depend."

"I am sorry, sir."

"Tell your aunt I will call this evening to write a letter for her."

Having memorized Flying Officer Tracy's identity card, Aunt Paulette was now repeating it for the third time to the schoolmaster, who, ostensibly, was writing a letter for the old lady but repeating to himself the details being given to him.

"The Boches are not certain that anybody parachuted down," he said, "but we must be extremely careful."

"I can only die once," retorted Aunt Paulette, "but before I do, I want to take some of the Nazis with me."

Suddenly she stiffened. She brought out a cheap construction set from a cupboard and handed it to Pierre, who promptly busied himself building a bridge.

Two motorcyclists had arrived at the front door, a Nazi lieutenant and a sergeant. They entered the cottage.

"Madame Labiche?" asked the officer.

"Yes, that's me," answered the old lady.

"And who are you?" asked the lieutenant. "Do you live here?"

"No. I'm Monsieur Henri Duplay, the schoolmaster—"

"And what harm is he doing?" shrieked Aunt Paulette. "He is writing a letter for me to my only granddaughter in the Alsace, from whom I have not heard in three months. I have no education, I cannot write, and it would take a long time to make signs to my deaf-and-dumb nephew"—she pointed to Pierre who appeared indifferent to everything around him—"and for him to put words on paper. Besides, poor Pierre, he is not quite right here"—she tapped her forehead. "So the schoolmaster, Monsieur Duplay, may God bless and preserve him, writes the letter for me."

"May I see that?" asked the officer, putting out his hand for the letter.

"Certainly, there is nothing confidential in it."

And, indeed, the officer read a plaintive, gossipy letter to "My dear granddaughter," which included a paragraph praising the German army of occupation for their tact and kindness to the inhabitants of the village.

"I see that you are a sensible woman," remarked the lieutenant, handing back the letter. "And now I want to go over the house."

"Certainly," said Aunt Paulette. "It is not a showplace, but it has been my home since I was brought here as a bride."

"You stay here," ordered the lieutenant to the sergeant.

While the old woman took the officer around the cottage, the schoolmaster read the message in Pierre's eyes. Neither of them had as yet killed a man, but if it became necessary, it would have to be done. The airman could not be handed over. The large bread knife lying on the table beside the loaf would be an ideal weapon for one of them.

To make sure that the message had been correctly read, Pierre demonstrated the sharp edge of the knife by cutting himself a slice of bread. He also took out his jack knife and sharpened a pencil.

The officer had now arrived at the back of the cottage.

"What is that?" he asked, pointing to the woodshed.

"That's the woodshed," and Aunt Paulette opened the door, "but that you will have to inspect alone, if you enjoy the company of wild rats."

The officer instinctively stepped back, and the old woman quickly closed the door. They reentered the cottage.

"As you have a spare room," said the lieutenant, "and as your cottage is so lonely and near the sea, we have decided to billet Sergeant Katzenbacher with you."

The sergeant clicked his heels.

Thursday night was the one night in the week when the village choir, which was famous in the Calvados area, and, indeed, throughout Normandy, was allowed to break the curfew, and to stay out until eleven o'clock, in order to rehearse in the local inn.

It was a concession given by the German commandant in the hope of getting some cooperation, particularly as all the notables of the village—the doctor, the pharmacist, the priest, the schoolmaster—were all members of the choir. Two Gestapo agents were always present to see that nothing subversive, even in talk, could take place.

Pierre, always the willing horse, was there as an additional "barman" to help with the drinks and the dishwashing.

Rehearsals were over, and fifteen minutes were allowed before closing time. Pierre was taking a tray full of drinks to a table, when a Gestapo man put out a foot, tripped Pierre, and sent him flying. Liquor and broken glasses were all over the floor. The pharmacist ran forward to pick Pierre up, and to assure himself that he was all right.

Nobody said a word to the Nazis. The two men of the Master Race puffed at their cigars, as the proprietor of the inn gave a display of anger to impress the Gestapo men. He upbraided Pierre for being a clumsy idiot. Turning to the schoolmaster, he said, "Tell the boy to put the music and the piano accordion away. He knows where they go, and warn him that he'll be sacked if he can't do better."

The schoolmaster signaled the message, and Pierre took the music books and the piano accordion up the stairs. After the first floor, he moved as swiftly as he could to the attic.

Once inside he quickly put his load down, and rapped a prearranged signal on the roof trapdoor with a broom handle. The door opened and a tiny basket was lowered. Pierre took a small rolled-up pellet from his mouth, and put it in the basket which was lifted up.

By the time Pierre was back in the inn the story of Flying Officer Tracy was being transmitted by wireless to the British.

As the villagers left the inn, a radio detector truck rushed up to make a search. However, the wireless operator had left five minutes before, and was now well away to set up a new post.

Five days later Gabrielle gave Pierre a written message from her father, the pharmacist.

"Your aunt's medicine is ready."

After school, Pierre went to the pharmacy. He collected a bottle, and was also given a small piece of paper in which were two pills. The pharmacist showed him a strip of paper on which was written, "Tonight at eleven; use both pills." Pierre nodded acknowledgment, and once again the paper was used as a spill to light a cigarette dangling from Monsieur Renaud's lips.

The kitchen clock struck ten. Aunt Paulette was darning socks. Pierre was working on his construction set, and Sergeant Katzenbacher was writing a letter to his family in Cologne.

The old lady yawned, put down the sock, observed that tomorrow was another day, and announced that she was going to bed. She embraced Pierre, and said "Good night" to the German, who rose promptly, clicked his heels, and like an automaton said, "Heil Hitler."

Barely had the old woman left the room than Pierre and the sergeant began what had obviously become a little nightly conspiracy. Pierre brought his set over to the German, and from a barrel in the corner of the room he drew a large mug of cider for the sergeant, and a smaller one for himself.

This had been a routine for the past four nights, and the sergeant enjoyed it. He had become very fond of Pierre, and the lad apparently reciprocated this friendly feeling. Pierre reminded him of his own son, Franz. He showed Pierre pictures of his wife and son. It was fun helping this deaf and dumb boy with his toy. It was like being at home.

As he put the pieces together, the sergeant took deep drafts of the cider. The old woman certainly knew how to brew a worthwhile drink. It was even better than the canteen beer. He finished the mug, smacked and wiped his lips with satisfaction, and, before he could refuse, Pierre had filled the mug again.

"Why not," said Sergeant Katzenbacher. True, he felt just a trifle drowsy, but never let it be said that a German soldier, a sergeant of the Master Race, couldn't down a couple of mugs of French cider.

Pierre watched him closely as the sergeant found it difficult at first, and then impossible, to fit the pieces of the toy together. He began a mumbled swearing to himself, and then, suddenly, without a word of warning, he slumped across the table, completely unconscious. The pharmacist's pills had done their job well.

Aunt Paulette was in the cellar, saying good-bye to Flying Officer Tracy, having first made sure that the German soldier was completely out.

"Make it *au revoir,* Aunt Paulette. I will never forget you and Pierre, and if I survive this war, and you and Pierre do, remember that there is always a home for both of you in America, if you ever want one. Please tell this to Pierre. He is the bravest boy that I have ever known. Tell him he is my friend for life, the greatest friend any man ever had."

He unstrapped his wristwatch.

"Give Pierre—"

"No," interrupted the old lady. "No souvenirs, no sign of your visit. Come, it is time to go up. The men will be punctual."

As the kitchen clock struck eleven, two men, dressed as fishermen, in unrelieved black, emerged from the darkness, outside the woodshed.

"Can I say good-bye to Pierre?" whispered Tracy.

"No, he is on guard. We must not disturb him. Good-bye, good luck, God bless you."

The next second the three men had vanished into the night.

"And now to put the Boche to bed," murmured Aunt Paulette, and she smiled.

Three days later, after prayers had been said in school, Gabrielle, the pharmacist's daughter, put up her hand.

"Yes, Gabrielle?" asked the schoolmaster.

"Please, sir, my father says can you please tell him if the words *'L'avenir, l'avenir, l'avenir c'est à moi'* (The future, the future, the future belongs to me) come from a poem? He came across it last night."

"Why, yes Gabrielle. Let me write the line on the blackboard." He did so.

"And tell your father that it comes from a Victor Hugo poem on Napoleon."

Only Pierre and the schoolmaster knew the silent message that flashed between them. A great joyous smile spread over Pierre's face. Another Allied airman had arrived back safely to carry on the fight for freedom.

THE THREE DANISH MUSKETEERS

To THEIR INTIMATES in Copenhagen they were known as the Three Danish Musketeers—Niels, Frederick, and Sven, inseparable thirteen-year-old schoolmates.

Physically and mentally they were older than their years, and in character and temperament they were as different as three boys could be. Niels, as befitted the son of the skipper and owner of a fishing boat—whose ancestors had been seamen for centuries—was down-to-earth and practical. Frederick, son of a master craftsman who made lovely furniture, was a sensible dreamer. Nail-biting Sven, son of a taxi driver, was a worrier, but once he got his teeth into something he would not let go. And the three boys had two characteristics in common—courage, and a deep love for King and country. The fathers of the "Three Musketeers" were allied in as close a friendship as were the boys.

The ninth of April, 1940, dawned as the blackest day of their lives. Without warning and with protestations of great friendship, the Nazis had invaded Denmark. The German coal ships that had arrived the previous night in Copenhagen were found to contain German soldiers in their holds. Paratroopers had landed at key points.

By the time the three boys had arrived at school, the very brief resistance was over, and Germany had occupied Denmark, bringing to an end an independence that had lasted for more than a thousand years.

"Behave yourselves," said the Nazis, "and nothing will happen to you."

The iron hand was in a thick velvet glove. Here was a wealthy country, rich in dairy produce, which was to be the showpiece of Hitler's Europe, but the Nazis reckoned without men like the fathers of the "Three Musketeers," and without the boys themselves. The fathers became the nucleus of a Resistance Group in Copenhagen. Nature had made Denmark an ideal place for Resistance Groups, with a coastline of 5,500 miles and with 500 islands.

The boys could not be kept in ignorance of their fathers' group, but they were kept at arm's length from its activities. The men were not going to endanger their children. It was risky enough as it was.

But the boys refused to be idle. They founded a "Churchill Club" in school, the object of which was to make life unpleasant for the Nazis. They stole arms from the soldiers whenever an opportunity presented itself, and indulged in small acts of sabotage, even disobeying their parents. They wore DKS badges, as members of *Den Kolde Skulder Club* (the Cold Shoulder Club), which frowned on any kind of fraternization with the Nazis.

"I'm fed up with this kind of resistance," said Sven. "Months have passed and we've done little that is worthwhile. I don't like being treated like a kid. Let's have it out with our fathers. Let's form our own group."

The three boys confronted their fathers.

"We know you've got a Resistance Group. Why are we kept out of it? We're not children any longer. The Nazi invasion has made us grown-ups. Surely you can make use of us. There must be many worthwhile things that we can do, and so save you time and trouble."

After quite an argument, they decided to admit the boys to a kind of second team, unknown to any other members of the Group.

Their main job was to act as runners, with messages for other groups. These had headquarters all over town and in scores of other places like Elsinore, Lyngby, and Humlebaek.

The boys took their messages to bookshops, to inns, to tobacco shops, to schools, to art galleries, and they learned to be cautious. If, for example, a copy of Hans Andersen's *Fairy Tales* was prominently displayed in the window of a bookshop, it meant that there was no danger. If the *Life of Bismarck* was well displayed, the message was "Keep out, the Gestapo are nosing around."

The place the boys liked best was a ship chandler's shop on the waterfront. This was run by a distant relation of Niels' family, who was fondly called Uncle Erik. It was he who had christened the boys the Three Danish Musketeers. A red-faced, white-haired ex-Navy man, Uncle Erik was born laughing, and his loud jolly laugh was infectious, especially if anybody complained about the foul tobacco that he smoked in his foul pipe.

To Uncle Erik the boys told their inmost thoughts. "We're no longer schoolboys," they told him. "Being messenger boys is all very well—"

"Don't decry the work you are doing," interrupted Uncle Erik. "It is just as essential as any kind of sabotage. We could not do our work efficiently without you."

"That's all very well," countered Sven, "but we've done this for a long time now, and we would like to show our parents that we're grownup enough to do a bit of real sabotage ourselves."

"When do your school holidays begin?" asked Uncle Erik.

"This weekend," came the answer.

"Good. Come to me on Monday morning, but keep this quiet."

Early Monday morning the boys arrived at the ship chandler's shop. He gave them a slip of paper on which was a man's name and the address of a factory making important electrical components.

"They need all the help they can get at this factory," explained Uncle Erik. "You will be given menial jobs, carrying things from one shop to the other, sweeping the floor and so on. Report to the foreman whose name I have given you, and he will hire you. Then Frederick, before you go to work on Thursday, I want you to come and see me. You will be given the job of sweeping the factory floor. Is that clear?"

The boys agreed that everything was quite clear.

They reported to the foreman and were hired, with Frederick as the floor sweeper.

Early Thursday morning he reported to Uncle Erik, who had prepared a special lunchbox for him, and then proceeded to give him detailed instructions.

At eleven thirty that morning, a cigarette dangling from his mouth, and carrying a brush and bucket, Frederick entered the "holy of holies," the control room.

The engineer in charge almost had a fit.

"Don't you know that nobody must smoke in this factory, and especially here. Are you mad?"

Frederick put out his cigarette on the floor.

"I'm sorry, sir, I'm new here, but I'm such a smoker that I almost become ill if I don't have a few puffs."

"A bit young for such an addiction, but, alas, I understand," was the sympathetic reply. "I'm like that myself."

"Especially when it's an American cigarette, smuggled in from Sweden," said Frederick, producing the packet. "Please have some, sir," and Frederick gave him half of the packet, which was accepted almost greedily.

As he pocketed them he whispered to Frederick: "I must go out to the lavatory for a few minutes. If anybody asks for me, tell where I am, and say I won't be a moment."

Within the next ten seconds, Frederick had fished out his lunchbox from the bottom of his bucket, moved a switch in it, and placed it where Uncle Erik had directed him.

Two minutes later, having enjoyed a few puffs, the engineer returned. He thanked Frederick for having "minded the shop."

At twelve thirty, when there was a fifteen-minute break between shifts, and the factory was empty, except for the men in the canteen, there occurred a terrific explosion in the control room. Fire soon spread, and within a few minutes at least half the factory was destroyed.

"Do you know," said Uncle Erik, "the King was very pleased about your work at the factory? He congratulates you."

Uncle Erik said it so seriously that the boys never knew whether it was true, or whether it was a joke. They almost expected the King to speak to them when he took his daily ride on horseback from the Palace. He shook hands with them, as he did with many others of his people. They loved the way he ignored the Nazi salutes.

But Uncle Erik showed his own personal appreciation of what the boys had done by giving each a wrist compass, and buckling it on each boy's wrist with great ceremony. From their parents they received no praise, but they knew. Uncle Erik swore that he never told them. Could it have been the foreman, or even the control engineer who told?

The next effort of the First Eleven, as the boys called their father's Resistance Group, ended in disaster. Two of the Group were detailed to sabotage a factory making munitions. Every detail was prepared with the greatest care. They had a pass key to a back door, which led to a basement corridor, leading to the storerooms.

The two saboteurs arrived. They opened the door, walked along the corridor, and as soon as they entered the storeroom, it was flooded with light and they were surrounded by armed Nazi soldiers and Gestapo men. Before the two Resistance men could draw the guns they carried, they were shot down.

There could be no doubt that somebody had tipped off the Nazis. Was there an informer in the Resistance Group? They were the only people who knew of the planned sabotage.

At this time, the BBC from London was encouraging the Resistance men to strangle German transport. The fathers of the "Three Musketeers" realized that this might be a heaven-sent chance to discover if there was an informer in their Group. They had not replaced the two dead men, and of the remaining five they were more or less certain about three.

At the next meeting of the Group, held, as it nearly always was, in the pastor's house, it was decided that two of their Group, experts in railway sabotage, would join three men in Elsinore, to derail and blow up a train full of iron ore coming from Sweden.

On the day fixed for this sabotage, the three boys were sent to Elsinore in the late afternoon, to make careful inquiries. The first call was to Niels' uncle, a younger brother of Niels' father, who owned a fishing boat in Elsinore.

"Have you noticed anything unusual, Uncle, in the last hour or two?" asked Niels.

"If you call a number of Gestapo swine unusual, then I have. They try to pose like ordinary travelers, but you can tell them when they order a drink, or ask you a question."

Frederick obtained the same information from the hotel proprietor, and Sven confirmed all this from his conversation with his friends on the railway. Niels phoned his father, and in a carefully worded code message, gave him the vital information.

With the agreement of his two close friends, Niels' father decided to say nothing to the other members of the Resistance Group. The two saboteurs were told the truth, and were informed that they would set out for Elsinore in the usual manner, but would leave the train before it reached its destination, and would return to Copenhagen, an hour or two later, to attend a meeting of the Group.

The Elsinore Group was informed that the whole operation was off.

The iron ore train from Sweden made its usual uneventful run that night, much to the disappointment of swarms of Gestapo men, and truckloads of SS men.

The Copenhagen Group met in the pastor's house. There seemed to be absolutely no doubt now that one of the Group was a traitor. It had been narrowed down in the minds of the three principals to one of two men, Ole K——, or Uffe L——.

While the Group held its solemn meeting, the "Three Musketeers" were sent on an important mission. They were to burglarize Ole K——'s house. Nobody would be at home, because Ole K—— had told everybody that he had sent his two children and wife to Jutland, to join her sister on a farm.

Sven and Frederick were on guard back and front, while Niels forced a back window, and entered the house. Using a flashlight, he made his way to the living room. One wall was lined with bookshelves, and it was evident that a woman's touch was missing. There was dust all along the shelves, except in one spot, in front of a volume of *Shakespeare's Plays*. This intrigued Niels. He took the volume out, and discovered, to his great astonishment, that it was not a book at all. It was a box, enclosed by fake covers, so often used for cigarettes or cigars. It had a lock, but Niels did not hesitate to force it.

The contents evoked a low whistle of surprise from the boy. There were Danish bank notes to the amount of 100,000 kroner, a draft on a German bank for 50,000 marks, a list of telephone numbers—it was discovered later that each number connected with a

Gestapo chief, and, most incriminating of all, a contract for the sale of the house. Also, there was a letter from Ole K——'s wife, from a Munich address, congratulating him on selling the house and furniture so quickly, and telling him how happy she would be when he joined her and the children. She advised speed, and finished with the Nazi greeting, "Heil Hitler!"

Wrapping the "book" in a Nazi newspaper that was lying about, Niels made his exit as quickly as possible. The three boys were breathless when they arrived at the pastor's house.

It was the pastor himself who admitted them, and to him Niels showed the contents of the "book," and told him where he had found it.

"This needs careful management," said the pastor. "The Group is meeting inside. We must do nothing that arouses any suspicion. You stay here while I call out Niels' father."

Casually, the pastor apologized for interrupting the meeting, saying that a messenger had come about some fishing nets, and wanted Niels' father's advice. He wouldn't keep him a moment. Coffee would be brought in, right away.

Niels' father was furious. He gave instructions to the three boys, who were to bring in the coffee to the "Church elders," for that was what the Group was supposed to be.

The men were quite happy as each had a cup placed before him. The pastor put some crackers on the table, and Niels and Frederick stood behind Ole K—— as Niels' father unwrapped *Shakespeare's Plays* and put it in the center of the table. The amusing remarks of one or two of the Group were soon cut short. Before Ole K—— could reach his coat pocket, Niels and Frederick had each seized an arm, and held it behind the traitor's back, while Sven went through his pockets. He fished out two capsules, doubtless containing a deadly poison.

Twenty minutes later, the three boys carried a very large "parcel"—Ole K—— gagged and bound, completely wrapped in a dark blanket, and well covered with large fishing nets—down to Niels' father's boat. The rest of the Group was there, dressed as fishermen about to go out on a trip. They were ready to cast off, when a German car drove up and lit up the boat with a searchlight. Was the fear that held the Group about to be put to the test? Had the traitor betrayed them all, or was he handing them over to the Nazis one at a time?

"What are you doing there?" shouted the Nazi officer.

"We're just going out for a night's work," answered the skipper.

"A bit late, isn't it?"

"Well, we took the advice of the Fishery Superintendent. He said that it wouldn't be worthwhile until late at night. We can't afford to drift about for nothing."

"OK. Carry on."

The searchlight was switched off, and the car drove away.

Two hours later, after the "parcel" had been dropped overboard, and a fair catch of fish was in the boat, they returned to Copenhagen. It was the first time that the Three Danish Musketeers had seen a man murdered. They felt appreciably older than their years when the boat tied up.

The First Eleven Group decided to break up. Nobody was certain what the Gestapo really knew through the dead Ole K—— and each member joined a different Resistance Group. Uncle Erik saw to the details.

The fathers warned their three sons to lie low, but the boys had no intention of dissolving their own Group. The Second Eleven had now become the First Eleven. Uncle Erik also advised them to take it easy for a spell. The Nazis were becoming more bestial than ever. A saboteur who had been caught had been tortured unmercifully. His fingers were broken, he had one eye put out, and as a further refinement, salt and pepper had been put in his food, and no water was given him.

Yet what could the "Three Musketeers" do when Uncle Erik told them that two RAF pilots, who had been shot down and had been hidden by various Resistance Groups, had to be smuggled out to Sweden? They were at the moment in hiding with the ship chandler.

Sven undertook the job. He had friends among the railwaymen who worked on the ferry crossing for trains coming from Sweden to Denmark full of iron ore, but returning the other way with empty, but locked, trucks. There was always a wait at Elsinore, while trains were loaded onto the ferries.

Sven made the journey to Elsinore, made contact with his friends, and arranged for the two British pilots to be put up in a hotel until the appropriate moment.

That evening two men and Sven, wearing railway uniforms, took the train from Copenhagen to Elsinore. The two men had papers identifying them as Danish railway workers. The journey was uneventful. The men smoked foul cigarettes, and nobody cared to converse with dirty railway laborers.

Arriving at Elsinore, they were quickly led by Sven to the hotel, where they were locked in an attic. Ten minutes before the vital time, Sven had the two men by his side, busily helping with the ferry train. Just then a quarrel broke out fifty yards away, among a group of railwaymen. Voices were raised, there was swearing and cursing, and scores of men appeared to be involved in wanting to fight, or in trying to prevent a fight.

All the Nazi watchdogs immediately rushed to the scene. Quick as lightning, Sven broke the lock of one of the empty trucks, opened the door just wide enough for the two RAF pilots to squeeze in— heard a murmured "Thanks, pal"—closed the door and busied himself as a railway worker should.

Strangely enough, the quarrel among the men subsided as quickly as it had begun. The train started on time. Sven heaved a sigh of relief as it went on its way to Sweden, where, barely three miles away, a representative of the British Consul in Sweden, informed by Uncle Erik, would be waiting to welcome two British pilots.

By August, 1943, the Nazis were becoming ruthless. In a land which once "flowed with milk and honey" there were food shortages. The Nazis were taking all they could lay their hands on.

The Danes were becoming more restive. There was no doubt now who was going to win the war. The German victories had come to an end with the catastrophe at Stalingrad, the defeat in North Africa, and the invasion of Sicily.

On the twenty-eighth of August the Nazis issued an ultimatum to the Danish Government, virtually depriving the Danes of all their freedom. This was rejected, and the next day the Nazis took over the country, and a State of Emergency was declared. King Christian X declared himself a prisoner of war, and the order was given to the Danish Navy to scuttle or escape to Sweden. In no time the Danish Navy was no more.

All this excited the "Three Musketeers," but they longed for some positive action by themselves.

An opportunity was soon to present itself.

There was obviously something brewing when, during September, 1943, the Nazis ordered all ships and small boats not being used for commercial purposes to be removed from the Danish coasts and brought at least a thousand feet inland. This, of course, did not apply to fishing boats.

It had always made the Nazi Führer mad that Denmark had refused to subscribe to his policy of exterminating the Jews. To the Danes, a man or woman was a Dane, irrespective of his or her religion.

But now, as so often before, Hitler declared that his patience was exhausted. Arrangements were made secretly to round up the eight thousand Jews living in Denmark, and to transport them to concentration camps. The date fixed was the first of October, because this coincided with the Jewish New Year, and the Jewish families would be at home celebrating the holiday. A lightning raid would collar the lot.

Secret preparations had to be made days beforehand. Special Gestapo chiefs and SS Commandos arrived from Germany. One man who had to be informed was Georg Duckwitz, who was in charge of German shipping in Denmark. He was ordered to prepare the transport for the shipments of the Jews. He immediately leaked the news to trustworthy friends. Some prominent members of the Jewish community refused to believe it. It was not until the day before D day that any real action was taken. The rabbi told his congregation not to stay in the synagogue and pray, but to seek out their gentile friends and hide with them until they could escape to Sweden, which had promised to give asylum to any refugee, Jew or gentile.

Senior Danish police officers gave lists of names and addresses of the victims-to-be to the pastor. He enlisted the help of the "Three Musketeers" and their fathers. The news spread through Copenhagen and through Denmark like wildfire, and, with the exception of a small percentage of Danish Nazis, the whole country became one Resistance Group.

Niels, Frederick, and Sven collected Jewish families and brought them to hiding places. Sven's father's taxi carried the Jewish families into welcoming gentile homes. The pastor had twenty people crammed into his rooms. Niels' father's boathouse provided shelter for a dozen.

During a short interval, Frederick looked at a very serious Sven.

"Why are you biting your nails, Sven?"

"I was wondering if our classmate, Jacob, is a Jew. I've had tea in his house a couple of times, but I could never tell if his family is Jewish. They look like us."

"Why not go and see?" suggested Frederick.

Sven found a very distracted family. Jacob's father had received the warning, but would not face up to the ghastly truth.

"We have been here for generations and generations," he explained to Sven. It needed all Sven's persuasive arguments to get him and his family to agree to leave.

"You know where I live," said Sven to Jacob. "Bring with you only the absolutely essential things. Come to my house at four o'clock. I'll be there to meet you. Bring your mother and one sister first, and then your father and the other little sister. See you later, Jacob."

After a telephone call by his father, Niels was called off his roundup to go to Bispebjerg Hospital on a special mission. Sven's father took him there, and Niels informed the porter that Professor X—— had sent for him, which was not exactly true. But this was an emergency, and a white lie could be forgiven. He was shown into the professor's office, where a senior nursing sister awaited him. She introduced herself to Niels.

"I understand that the professor sent for you," said the sister. "It's most unusual that I shouldn't have known about it. But at the moment he is in the operating theater. Can I do anything for you?" Niels blushed. He thought quickly. Should he tell the sister or not? He decided to trust her.

"No, thank you Sister—the truth is that the professor did not send for me. I have been sent by my father to see him on a very important matter. It's urgent!"

"Is it medical?"

"No, Sister, it is personal, and it is terribly urgent."

"Perhaps I can help you," said the sister. "Is it to do with the proposed roundup of the Jews?"

"Yes, Sister."

"Then I'm afraid that you've come in vain. The head of the hospital, many of his colleagues, I myself, have all tried to persuade the professor to go away, at any rate for the time being, but he refuses. He is really only half Jewish. His mother was Christian, though he never denies being a Jew if he is called one. He is married to a Christian, and his young boy, David, is Christian. So he feels sure that the Nazis won't bother him. Besides, he says that he has so much to do in the hospital.

"Don't think we haven't tried to persuade him. We've taken it seriously, here. We are admitting hundreds of Jews, making them patients, doctors, orderlies and nurses, and hiding all we can in spare rooms until they can get to Sweden."

"But you don't understand, Sister."

There were tears in Niels' eyes as the words poured from him in a torrent.

"Our family worships the professor. He saved my mother's life—"

"He has saved many lives," interpolated the sister.

"I know. We would willingly lay down our lives for him. Don't you see that he mustn't take chances with these Nazis? They are losing the war, and they will take their revenge on anybody with the tiniest drop of Jewish blood."

"I hear the professor coming. You will have a chance to persuade him yourself."

The professor was delighted to see Niels. "Hello, Niels, this is a nice surprise. Is everything all right?"

"With the family, yes, sir."

The professor smiled. He looked at Niels as he asked the next question.

"Then why, Niels?"

"Please, sir, my father has sent me to plead with you to leave

Copenhagen today. If you don't think it's necessary for your family to leave, please, please leave alone."

The professor looked at the sister. Had she been plotting with Niels? She read his look.

"No, professor, we are not in league, but I agree with the young man one hundred percent."

"Please, professor, father is planning to take sixty people across to Sweden tonight. He begs you to join them. We have them well hidden at the moment. He also asked me to say that there are fourteen young children among them. If they cry—"

The professor went to a cabinet and took out a small box which he gave to Niels. "One tablet dissolved in a little water or milk will put a baby to sleep for four to five hours. Give it to the children an hour before you intend to sail, and warn the parents not to worry when they see their babies unconscious.

"As for me, Niels, tell your father not to worry. They won't interfere with me. I've too much work to do here. But also tell your father that I am grateful and proud of his friendship, as I am of yours, Niels. Keep in touch with me, Niels, and let me know how you get on, and if you need money don't hesitate to ask me for it. I know that nobody has said 'No' to the pastor."

The hold of the fishing boat was crammed with forty-six silent, anxious refugees, and fourteen unconscious babes cradled in their mothers' arms.

The "Three Musketeers" and their fathers were busy on deck preparing for the usual fishing trip. The pastor was a casual spectator, apparently showing no more interest in Niels' father's boat than in any of the other boats ready to sail.

Out went the little armada of fishing boats in the normal way. There was a wave of the hand from the pastor, who turned for home with a fervent prayer in his heart. Just seventeen miles to safety and happiness. May God grant it to them.

It was a happy boat returning from Malmo to Copenhagen. The crew had earned the right to sing gay sea chanteys. The fish were biting, and the hold that so recently held its human freight was now being loaded with fish.

A mile outside Copenhagen a German patrol vessel halted the

boat. "What have you been doing?" asked the German captain.

"That's a strange question to ask a fisherman," answered Niels' father. "If you care to go down in the hold you will see a fine catch of fish. Many a housewife is going to be glad in the morning."

"Have you been to Sweden?" came the next question.

"Now what would I be doing in Sweden? I can't land my catch there, and I don't like trespassing in other peoples' water."

"Show me your papers."

These were handed over.

Had the crew been too optimistic? Were they on a Gestapo list? Did the traitor of their onetime Group betray them all?

The moments of tension seemed long as the Nazi captain examined the papers, and then handed them back.

"OK. Carry on."

When the boat was tied up the crew held a hurried meeting; at least the fathers did. They decided to act in future with the greatest caution, and to send the "Three Musketeers" to Elsinore, to Niels' uncle, Aage, since the boys flatly refused to become lookers-on. "You are disobedient, Sven," said his father, and the other two men said the same to their sons.

"What would you do," asked Frederick's father, "if you were in my position and you had a son of your own?"

"I would do exactly what you have done, Father," replied Frederick, "and I would hope that my son would disagree with me, as I have done with you."

The boys had never been so active in their lives as they were with Niels' uncle. What an exciting time! Uncle Aage certainly understood their feelings. The days were spent hiding the hunted Jewish Danes in various seaside towns along the coast, in the woods, and in places inland. Uncle Aage knew all the tricks, and his enthusiasm for saving lives was an inspiration to the "Three Musketeers."

Elsinore, just two and three-quarter miles from Hälsingborg in Sweden, was becoming an impossible place to work in. Every day more Nazis were sent to Elsinore. They were all over the area. Small places along the coast and open beaches were now used for embarkation.

The "Three Musketeers" were happy. They were in their element. They had that night cheated the Nazis of eighty of their would-be victims. They had tied up in Elsinore, and were helping Uncle Aage to clean up the boat. They had also heard that the big Nazi roundup so far had resulted in the capture of a couple of hundred Jews out of Denmark's eight thousand.

The happy atmosphere in the boat suddenly vanished at the sight of a man standing on the quay. He asked for Uncle Aage, and appeared to be in a dreadful state. He was the perfect example of the hunted man suffering from shock. He mentioned the name of a man in Lyngby—of unimpeachable character—who had told him to go to Uncle Aage. He looked carefully around before he spoke.

"I understand that you are taking Jews across to Sweden. I am not a Jew, but a saboteur with a price on my head. See."

From his breast pocket he drew out a wallet, and with trembling fingers he pulled out a clipping from a newspaper. The heading was: "50,000 kroner, dead or alive," and there was his photograph. As he handed the clipping to Uncle Aage, the wallet dropped from his trembling fingers into the boat. Niels picked it up, and handed it to the thankful man.

"Don't think that I want you to take any risk without payment. Friends have provided me with money, now that I am ill and unable to carry on my sabotage with the Resistance. Here, take this five thousand kroner. I will give you another five thousand tonight. Where shall I meet you?"

"We sail from Humlebaek tonight. Be in the Church Hall at nine o'clock. Meanwhile, make yourself scarce."

"I will. I will. Thank you for your help. Until tonight."

As he left, Niels whispered to Sven: "Follow him, and report when you are satisfied."

Sven was off like a shot.

"Weren't you a bit quick to accept the man at his face value, Uncle Aage?" asked Niels.

"You don't think he's a wrong-un, do you Niels?" came the scared answer.

"I don't know, but the wallet he dropped was new and 'Made in Germany' was stamped on it, and the new kroner notes make me suspicious. Can I see some of them?"

Uncle Aage handed over a batch of notes. Niels held each one up to the light. In the right-hand corner of each note were the minutest pinpricks forming a pattern.

"I don't like the look of it, Uncle Aage, but we'll wait for Sven to return, and then we'll decide."

Meanwhile Sven had discreetly followed the stranger into Stengade, the busy shopping street. Before entering a tobacco shop, the stranger—no longer shell-shocked—spoke to a taxi driver.

As soon as the man entered the shop, Sven darted across the road. It was a Copenhagen taxi and Sven knew the driver. He knew practically every cab driver in Copenhagen.

"Hello, Hans, what are you doing in Elsinore?"

"Driving a bloody Nazi, I expect. I picked him up outside Dagmarhus, so I expect he's a dirty Gestapo chief. Now I've got to drive him back there."

"Thanks, Hans."

He crossed the road until the self-satisfied Nazi, smoking a cigar, the picture of happy health, got into the cab and drove off.

The distance to the boat was covered in record time, and a breathless Sven told his story. It threw Uncle Aage into panic. Had he betrayed scores of innocent people and many of his own fishing folk?

"Don't panic," said Frederick. "Tell us from whom you got your orders."

"The master of the school in Humlebaek," stammered Uncle Aage.

"Then leave it to us," answered the boy. "First go to the Bank. Can you trust the Bank manager?"

"With my life."

"Good, then tell him the whole story, and give him the money. He'll know what to do. Then tell the skippers of the other boats. How many are there?"

"Two," replied Uncle Aage.

"Tell them to rendezvous at Ringsted, an hour earlier than the original time. We'll meet you there. Come fellows, we must be off."

The next few hours were the most hectic the "Three Musketeers" had ever experienced in their young lives. They found the schoolmaster in Humlebaek who was responsible for this particular exodus, and with the help of the local pastor, and three sturdy housewives, they gathered every conceivable form of transport to take the refugees to Ringsted. They were collected from their hiding places, although some had to be persuaded to make the journey.

They felt that they had come to the end of the line. What was the use? They would never reach Sweden and safety, but the Danish women helpers calmed them, and foretold many happy years for them.

In Ringsted, the local people, sizing up the situation, quickly took the refugees into their homes. Niels, having had previous experience, made a note of those houses in which there were babies. He found a local doctor, a most sympathetic man, and he agreed to give each child an injection, an hour before sailing time.

Thirty minutes before zero hour, the fishing boats were at Ringsted. The refugees were shepherded to their boats, the parents carrying their unconscious children.

A bare ten miles away was safety and freedom. They made it.

Meanwhile a drama was being played out in Humlebaek. At a quarter to nine, two trucks filled with SS men, and two cars of Gestapo chiefs pulled up outside the Church Hall. The SS men surrounded the place, and the Gestapo men unceremoniously burst into the hall. It was not surprising that they stopped dead in the doorway. At a long refectory table, lit by candlelight, sat six pairs of chess players, facing each other, all intent on their next move.

The schoolmaster rose to welcome the intruders.

"Good evening, gentlemen, can I help you?"

"Where are the Jews?" barked the leading Gestapo officer.

"The Jews?" came the soft-spoken query. "We have no Jews here. This is the usual meeting of our chess club. . . ."

"Where are they?"—this was almost a shriek. "They were to meet here tonight to be taken to Sweden."

"I am afraid that somebody has sent you on a wild-goose chase."

"Search the place."

The Gestapo officers ransacked the place, the Church and the adjoining buildings. They drew a blank, as they did on the waterfront.

When the "Three Musketeers" returned to Elsinore, there was an urgent message awaiting them, recalling them to Copenhagen.

The situation was serious. Hitler and his Jew-murdering clique had been beaten. The "Berlin Bloodhounds" could claim no more in all than about four hundred out of the eight thousand Danish

Jews. Torture and bestiality became the order of the day. Machine-gunning innocent people became a commonplace affair.

They decided that anybody with a drop of Jewish blood would be roped in, and so the professor's name was on the list of those about to be sent to Theresienstadt concentration camp. The raid was to be at midnight.

A senior Danish police officer brought the news to Uncle Erik, who relayed it to the pastor and to Niels' father. The two of them went to the professor's home. He was at the hospital, operating, but he was due to return home for lunch, and his wife agreed to the plan outlined by the two men. She would on no account allow her husband to escape on his own.

"Please leave everything to us," said the pastor, "and ask your husband to wear his oldest suit."

At three o'clock that afternoon, the taxi driven by Sven's father drove up to the professor's house. Out sprang Niels, wearing a rather dirty work suit, and carrying a heavy suitcase.

Almost at the same time Frederick and Sven bicycled up to the house, parked at the back entrance, and busied themselves with the driver, ostensibly examining the engine of the taxi.

Inside the house Niels had given the professor a work suit, and a set of papers identifying him as a plumber who lodged with Uncle Erik.

"Can you ride a bicycle, sir?" asked Niels.

The professor laughed.

"Do you know a Dane who can't? I may be a bit out of practice, but I won't disgrace you."

Just then the doorbell rang. The professor and his wife looked at each other. She drew her son David close to her. Niels read the fear in their eyes.

"It's all right, sir. If there had been any danger, Sven's father would have warned us. He's waiting outside."

Niels opened the door to admit a young couple, who had obviously met Niels before.

"We meet again," said the young man. He introduced himself and his wife to the professor. He was the son of a famous banker, who was not unknown to the professor.

"My father sends you his best wishes. We are the young couple, newly married, who bought your house, including your car, furniture and the pictures, four weeks ago. You will see the date on this contract."

He handed the legal document to the professor.

"I must blush at the hard bargain I drove with you, especially over your lovely and valuable pictures, but if ever the Nazis get a sight of this contract, they will doubtless give me a good mark for having done you down, and will regret that they could not steal your treasures and ruin the property. Will you please sign it, there. We did not want to forge your signature unnecessarily."

The professor signed on the dotted line.

"We will keep it for you as if it were our own," said the young wife. "We look forward to the day when we can say to you, 'Welcome home!' "

"Thank you," said the professor's wife, "for your kindness in acting as caretakers. Let me give you a quick tour of the house before we leave."

"You will need money . . ." said the young man somewhat diffidently.

"Thank you," said the professor, "we are not short of money. Our friends are very kind."

When the women returned, Niels took charge. Good-byes were said, and the professor's wife and David joined Frederick and Sven in the taxi to be driven to Sven's home where they would be spending the night.

The professor and Niels mounted their bicycles, with the boy carrying the suitcase. They were soon lost in the stream of bicyclists returning home. They had passed the Cathedral, and were going along quite merrily when they were suddenly brought to a halt in the narrow street by a human barricade. Two lines of armed men barred the way, one line of SS men, backed by a line of HIPO (*Hilfspolitzei*—Danish-German Auxiliary Police). Two similar lines took up their positions at the other end of the street.

Every cyclist and civilian had to make an exit in single file, showing his identification papers to the Gestapo. A truck was ready to take away any person who seemed unsatisfactory. Outwardly calm, inwardly scared, Niels thought of every alarming possibility. No attempt had been made to alter the appearance of the professor. Could there be a member of the HIPO who was an ex-patient of the professor? Would he in gratitude remain dumb, or would he give the surgeon away?

Already there were six unfortunates in the truck, when Niels and the professor showed their papers. The suitcase was closely examined, but it contained only the innocent tools of a plumber, with, for good measure, a ball and chain of a lavatory cistern.

Their papers were handed back, and they were waved on.

Nobody could have grudged them the glass of schnapps they drank when they arrived at Uncle Erik's home.

The following morning, after a good breakfast, Uncle Erik gave them the news.

"First, professor, your wife and son, accompanied by Frederick and Sven as bodyguards, are by now well on the way to Stege in the island of Mön, in Sven's father's taxi, to be the guests of a retired university lecturer and his sister.

"Incidentally, Frederick and Sven are being tutored in history and German literature by the ex-lecturer, because they are backward in those subjects. Don't laugh, Niels, this is very serious," added Uncle Erik with his deep chuckle.

"Secondly, the hospital was raided last night. Everybody swore that they hadn't seen you for days, although the Nazis knew that you had operated in the morning.

"At midnight they raided your home, only to find an infuriated houseowner, who yelled at them unmercifully. He threatened to report them to the Reichskommissar. Believe it or not, the Nazis apologized and left with their tails between their legs.

"Thirdly, with the help of my friends in the police, we have spread three nice stories about you, professor. You were spotted in Odense last night—we chose that because, as you know, it was the home of Hans Andersen," Uncle Erik added with a laugh.

"You were positively seen outside Aarhus, where you were trying to persuade a fisherman to take you and your wife and child to Sweden. And an ex-patient caught sight of you in Aalborg, where you were trying to join your brother, who is in hiding. We thought it would be nice to give you a brother.

"You will note that we chose the biggest towns outside Copenhagen. That's to give the butchers and their bloodhounds plenty to do, especially as the archkiller, Adolf Eichmann, has turned up."

"You're a marvel, Uncle Erik," said Niels.

"No, I just like a bit of fun. Now, for your own plan. Your ultimate destination will—at present—be Stege in the island of Mön. We think that that is the safest place, because every Nazi between Gilleleje in the north and Koge in the south, has been alerted. They have gone through Elsinore with a fine-tooth comb. If, by any chance, the Nazis go prowling around in Mön, you will be notified of a change of plan the night before you leave for Stege."

That evening, Sven's father came into Uncle Erik's shop to see the professor.

"Everything has gone according to plan," said the taxi driver. "Your wife and son are safely established on the island of Mön, and were given a very warm welcome by their hosts. They send their love and are looking forward to an early reunion. I must go. Call me if you need me."

"How long will we be before we start?" asked the professor.

"I know how anxious you must be to rejoin your wife and son," replied Uncle Erik, "but there is one more link in the chain from here to the island that has to be forged. I'm hoping for news tonight."

The good news came, and Uncle Erik outlined the plan. The two plumbers would bicycle to their first job two miles behind Koge. "Here is the name and address of the man who needs your help. You will find that something is wrong with the plumbing, just as you found one lavatory here almost in pieces. You will spend the night there, and your host will tell you where your next job is. I want you to take a good three days bicycling the one hundred and twenty kilometers [seventy-five miles] to the island. The country is very beautiful, and while you enjoy yourselves, I'll try and put the finishing touches to our plan. Have you enough money?"

"Yes, thank you," answered the professor.

"Well, Niels can always do with a little extra," and Uncle Erik stuffed a few kroner into the pocket of his suit.

They spent the first night with charming people, who had been waiting for them. They gave them the name and address of people a mile and a half behind the fishing village of Rodwig, who were sorely in need of their plumbing expertise.

The kindly family put them up for the night, and after a break-fast that would have been a sensation in Copenhagen, they were given the name and address of the people who needed them in Stege on the island of Mön.

The bicyclists, now in good form—so they said—put on speed. It was late afternoon when they reported to the house in Stege. Niels tactfully disappeared to join Frederick and Sven, while the professor was reunited with his family. For the next two days the professor remained close to the house, always the plumber ready to repair the cistern of the spare lavatory.

On the third day a surprise visitor turned up. It was Uncle Erik, fully equipped for a fishing holiday. His arrangements were com-plete. At twelve that night a Swedish motor boat would be off Ulf-shale, about five miles from Stege.

"Now you Three Musketeers," said Uncle Erik, "off you go to Ulfshale, and rustle up a row boat from somewhere, large enough to carry six."

"Here's the name of an old friend of mine," said their host with whom they had been staying. "Ask anybody in Ulfshale for Mor-gens the sailor, and they'll direct you to his cottage. Tell him that I sent you."

"When you find the boat," was Uncle Erik's parting shot, "see that it is in a safe place until we need it tonight."

The boys had no difficulty in finding old Morgens. He was an ancient mariner who chuckled when he heard about the quest for a row boat. He scented adventure since he knew that such boats were forbidden, but if it meant one in the eye for the Nazis he was their man even though he was ninety.

"You see that house there," he pointed to a large house, shut-tered and deserted, "the people who live there are now in Copenha-gen. They left here before the order came to move little boats a thousand feet inland. So the chances are that the row boat—I know they had one because I got it for them—is in the boathouse. Let's go up there and see. I'd better take a couple of tools with me, in case they have been careful enough to lock it."

The old sailor led the way to the house, explaining to the boys the alibi he had already thought of if a snooping Nazi turned up.

"We heard somebody walking round the house, and, to make

sure, we collared the boat to prevent its being used. We're good law-abiding citizens, we are," and he roared with laughter.

They needed no tools. The door to the boathouse was not locked, and there was the row boat.

"We'd better leave it here until we need it," suggested Frederick. "I vote that one of us goes back to report to Uncle Erik, while the other two remain here. Let's toss for it." They did. Frederick had to go back to Stege.

Two minutes to midnight. A tense, silent group on the seashore. From the sea came the low distant hum of a motor. Then silence.

Uncle Erik followed the second hand on the luminous dial of his wristwatch.

In the row boat the professor had a protective arm around his wife. Their son, David, was fast asleep. Niels and Frederick grasped the oars in readiness to move. Sven was at the tiller.

"Stop biting your nails, Sven, and watch carefully," whispered Uncle Erik, "I am about to signal. A bearing on your wrist compass might help. Is your own flashlight handy?"

"Yes, Uncle Erik."

The flashlight beamed the prearranged signal. Back, from half a mile out, came the answering light.

"Ready, boys?"

"Ready, Uncle."

Uncle Erik turned to the old sailor.

"Come on, Morgens. A good shove."

Out on the sea went the boat, with Niels and Frederick rowing skillfully, and as silently as they could. Uncle Erik and the old sailor watched them disappear into the night.

They stood transfixed until the low hum of a motor reached them. They looked at one another, smiled, and shook hands.

Then they waited for the "Three Musketeers" to return.

Early in May, 1945, with Denmark free again, the professor and his family returned from Sweden to their house to find their home in perfect condition. In every room there was a floral welcome, and across the living room was strung a banner on which the "Three Musketeers" had painted *"Velkommen til Danmark!"* ("Welcome to Denmark!")

❋

A red-letter day in the lives of the "Three Musketeers" came in 1950, when Sir Winston Churchill visited Copenhagen.

Relating their experience to Uncle Erik, Niels said, "We were introduced to Churchill."

"Were you really?" queried Uncle Erik with a disbelieving twinkle in his eye.

"Well, as a matter of fact," amended Frederick, "we pushed through the crowd and introduced ourselves."

"We told him," added Sven, "that we were the Three Danish Musketeers, and Churchill said 'Good for you, young fellows. One for all, and all for Denmark.' "

ALDO AND THE CONTESSA

THERE WAS absolutely no doubt that the most hated, most despised woman in Parma was the Contessa M——. When she walked through this ancient north Italian city, she was given a wide berth. If Aldo was with her, he was greeted enthusiastically by the Parmensi—as the natives of Parma love to be called—so as to emphasize the ostracism of the Noble Lady. Her entrance into a shop was the signal for a sudden silence, quite a feat where Italian women are concerned. Much as the shopkeepers enjoyed taking the Contessa's money, many of them would have preferred not to have her business.

Yet, in all fairness, the Parmensi grudgingly admitted that for a woman of seventy the Contessa was very lovely, had great dignity, and dressed as became a woman of her station. They also grudgingly admitted that she gave time and money to the sick and poor, but this they said was to salve her Fascist conscience.

The Contessa, the only child of Irish parents and heiress to a great fortune, had always kept her Irish sense of humor. At the age of twenty-one, on her first visit to Europe, she had fallen in love with Italy—"fathomless love," in the words of Lord Byron. She loved the people who were unashamed of their genuine emotions, and never tried to hide them. She also fell in love with the man she was to marry, Count M——, a member of the Diplomatic Corps, young, handsome, and rich, owner of two princely palaces, one on the outskirts of Rome, and one just outside Parma. Celebrities crowded the Contessa's salon. To be invited by the Contessa was the mark of social acceptance. And at seventy, she was still bewitching and witty.

In 1921, while the Count and Contessa were at their Parma home, tragedy struck. The Count was thrown from his horse, and killed. The Contessa closed her palace—she never lived in it again —and rented the first floor of a luxury hotel in Parma, furnishing it with some of her own treasures.

She preferred Parma to the fabulous city of Rome. She could spend hours walking around its picturesque piazzas, or meditating in the Cathedral, that remarkable Romanesque edifice, which was built in 1046. She adored the fresco, a masterpiece of Correggio, and the twelfth-century sculptures of Antelami. Every now and again restlessness took her to some corner of the world, but always in the end she returned to Parma.

When the Second World War broke out, the Contessa was in London. After one or two meetings with certain significant people, it was decided that she would be more useful in Parma than she would be in England.

It was then that she met Aldo, who was page boy in the hotel, at the beck and call of everybody.

"A shrimp of a lad"—the Contessa's expression—Aldo was small for thirteen, and it was a marvel that one so young could work as he did. Temperamental, as became an Italian boy, he enjoyed every moment of the day. Verdi, who was born near Parma, was his favorite composer, and he would empty wastepaper baskets to an aria from *Aïda,* or sweep the stairs to a melody from *Traviata.* His dark twinkling eyes were shaded by long lashes, which could have adorned any beautiful woman, in contrast to the determined mouth and chin, and the unruly mop of black hair, which defied the pomade Aldo lavishly rubbed on it.

The moment the Contessa saw Aldo, she decided to "appropriate" him. She liked his cheerfulness and his zest for work. She arranged with the proprietor of the hotel to pay his full wages, and to allow him to be the page boy for only two hours every day.

It was not an easy time for Aldo. Poor as his parents were, and much as they needed the money Aldo brought home, they did not like the idea of their son working for the Fascist Contessa.

"But Mamma," Aldo protested, "I work less than I used to do, and the Contessa is kind to me, and pays me much more than I used to get, as you well know."

"What do you think our neighbors say about us?" said Aldo's father. "Already some of them shut up when I join them. They think I, too, am a Fascist."

But nothing could shake Aldo's devotion to the Contessa. They formed an unbreakable aliance.

For the first few months the Contessa strove hard to keep Italy out of the war. But, alas, she could do little to prevent Mussolini stabbing France in the back when she was being overwhelmed by Hitler's Nazis.

On the tenth of June, 1940, when Mussolini declared war on France, the Contessa and Aldo secretly declared war on Nazi Germany and Fascist Italy. When the Contessa did not protest against the Nazi German commandant of the area, and his staff, occupying her palace—it would have made no difference if she had—the people of Parma chalked up another black mark against her.

The tenth of July, 1943. The tide had turned with a vengeance against the Nazis and the Fascists. The Allies had landed in Sicily. It was a day for quiet rejoicing, a day for Aldo to hum a triumphant aria from his favorite Verdi, but the boy was sad, and looked with gloomy eyes through the window of the Contessa's salon, to the street below.

"What is wrong, Aldo? You are not yourself today, a day for which we have worked and waited."

Aldo turned to face the Contessa, but he did not answer.

"I am still waiting, Aldo. Must I remind you that you and I have no secrets from one another?"

"I am sorry, Contessa. I am sad for two things. One, because Enrico, our wireless operator, has been taken by the Gestapo. I know he will not speak, so they will break and torture his body bit by bit."

"I am very sad about it, too," said the Contessa. "He was very brave, but very rash. When one gambles with one's life, one should be careful. He would not listen to advice. What is the second thing?"

"My brother, Orlando, has finally straggled back from the Russian front." There were tears in Aldo's eyes. "I did not recognize him at first. He was like a skeleton. His feet were torn and bloody. For boots he had dirty rags. He had been so proud, and when the defeat came the Nazis abandoned the Italian wounded, took all the transport for themselves, and left our men to find their way across Europe. Orlando is lucky to be alive. He is full of hatred now for the Nazis, and for our own country. He wants to desert."

The Contessa smiled.

"I hope that you have no objection to Orlando's deserting."

"No, Contessa, but we cannot keep him at home. He has been with us for three days. We are trying to put some flesh on his bones, but it is too dangerous for my father and mother to keep him in the house. He talks about joining the Partisans. I have not told him anything."

"You can arrange that for your brother. As he is a good Catholic, ask him to see Father Pietro. That will keep us out of it. You go to the father now, and tell him that you will bring your brother to see him an hour before curfew. Leave the rest to the holy father, and do as he says. Tomorrow I go to see my doctor in Milan. Anything else, Aldo?"

"Orlando is very angry with me that I work for you. He says that you are a Fascist aristocrat, a friend of Mussolini and Hitler. I told him that you are kind to me, and that you pay me well."

"A very good answer, Aldo, to everyone who blackens me."

"But it hurts, Contessa."

"Thank you, Aldo."

The Contessa made periodical visits to her doctor in Milan. By a strange coincidence her visits were usually followed by strikes at the big factories—more than twice as many in 1943 than in the previous year—or by sabotage of important railway yards or bridges. As the Contessa put it, this was pouring grit into the German war machine. Her favorite slogan was, "Not a workman, not another machine for Nazi Germany."

✿

Aldo took his brother Orlando to see Father Pietro, an elderly, kindly priest who had baptized both the brothers.

"I am happy to see you, Orlando," said the father, "even though it is difficult to recognize you."

"I am happy to be home, father, but I am in great torment."

"How can I help you, my son?"

"You know, father, that I am not a Communist or Fascist. I am a good Catholic, and after what I have been through on the Russian front, and seen how the Nazis behave to innocent people, I do not want to fight with them any more. For my own self-respect, I must desert."

"What do you want me to do, Orlando my son?"

"Aldo has told me about the Partisans. He says that they are fighting to liberate our country. Tell me, father, that I am not doing wrong in deserting and in joining the Partisans."

"If your conscience tells you, Orlando, that by joining the Partisans you are fighting for the freedom of your country, then you are doing no wrong."

"Then how can I join them?"

"Perhaps I could help," said the priest, "because I believe that the nearest Partisans are in the Apennines. Aldo could find out, but I could take you part of the way. Let me phone Giuseppe about his car."

The priest got his number.

"Giuseppe? Father Pietro here. I need your car for an errand of mercy. No, I know you have had a busy day. I don't want you to drive. I will do so myself. Just bring the car outside the Church. I will meet you—yes, now please."

Then, turning to Orlando, he said, "I think that by chance I may have something useful for you."

He left the room, and soon returned, to the great surprise of Orlando, carrying a gun and a box of ammunition.

"It might help you. As a soldier you would have had one. You are still a soldier."

Father Pietro had driven for two hours before he halted.

"This is where I leave you, my children. Aldo, although you are the younger, you must now take charge. I must make a call on some friends on the way home, in case some inquisitive person wants to know what I am doing abroad at this time of the night. God be with you, my sons, and good luck. You will, of course, come to see me, Aldo."

It took another hour of good footslogging before Aldo led his brother through a silent village, where not a man or beast stirred. A few hundred yards outside the village they came to an orchard, in the middle of which was a small, somewhat tumbledown house.

"This is it," whispered Aldo.

He tapped an arranged signal on a window. There was no response. He tapped again. Still no answer. Aldo's heart sank. What if the Nazis had rounded up Teresa and her mother? It would be a tremendous loss, an irreplaceable loss.

Aldo tapped again, a little more forcefully this time.

The window was opened a fraction.

"Who is it?"

"It is me, Aldo."

"One minute."

Two minutes later, Aldo and Orlando were in Teresa's kitchen.

To say that fifteen-year-old Teresa was beautiful is an understatement. She was a black-eyed goddess, and even at this unearthly hour, when she was awakened and was gracefully disheveled, she looked as fresh as a daisy.

While she busied herself preparing a meal, Aldo made up the fire. He was perfectly at home in Teresa's house, to the astonishment of Orlando.

"As quiet as you can, Aldo. We mustn't wake Mamma. I must say your brother Orlando is better looking than you. Are you still the lapdog of that Fascist Contessa?"

"I have spoken to him about it," said Orlando. "He must be hypnotized by the old so-and-so."

"Lay off me," said Aldo. "She is kind to me—"

"And the pay is good," added Teresa scornfully. "Always the same answer. I will get dressed while you two eat. Don't drink too much wine, Aldo—"

"I can hold my liquor as well as any man," retorted the boy.

"Big fellow!" was her laughing exit line.

The meal was over, Teresa and Orlando got ready for their march into the Apennines, where she would hand Orlando over to the Partisans.

"Mamma will be awake before I come back," she said to Aldo. "You will tell her that I have gone for a little walk. Then you can go to your usual stopping place on the main highway and thumb a lift from Arturo Borelli. He is always on the lookout. So long, Aldo"—and she planted a kiss full on his mouth—"and don't blush when I kiss you. *Arrivederci,* and come back soon."

"Did you have a successful trip?" asked the Contessa.

"Yes, Contessa."

"And was Teresa as rude as usual about me?" laughed the Contessa. "You don't like answering. And why do you always blush when we talk about Teresa?"

She enjoyed teasing Aldo about girls.

"She is very beautiful and she has a wonderful character. The only time we stopped there—you remember we needed water for the car—and she learned who I was, she was positively rude to me. She despised me, and you were almost in tears quarreling with her. Never mind, Aldo, I, too, love the girl. And now, back to work. I had a good time in Milan. My doctor found me in excellent condition and we have a replacement for the wireless operator. This is your next move." She gave Aldo detailed instructions.

At four o'clock that afternoon Aldo stood on the Verdi Bridge, gazing at the torrent. A stranger, carrying a small suitcase, approached him, and spoke to him in faultless Italian.

"Excuse me, young man, but this is the city famous for Parma violets?"

"Yes, sir," answered Aldo, "also famous for Parma ham."

"How enchanting. It is worth staying here. I have been hired as the headwaiter at this hotel"—he showed Aldo the name and address of the Contessa's hotel on a slip of paper—"perhaps you could direct me?"

"Better still," replied Aldo, "I can take you there."

On the recommendation of the Contessa, the new headwaiter, Luigi, had been hired by the proprietor, especially as he was a prospective buyer of the hotel. The owner wanted to return to his native Rome, since business was not too good, and was further hindered by a Fascist Contessa having a whole floor. Also there was always the chance of a stray bomb destroying the hotel.

Having served as deputy headwaiter in three of London's luxury hotels, Luigi certainly knew his job. According to his identity papers he was a Swiss who had also spent some time in Italy. After meeting the proprietor and making all the necessary arrangements, Luigi introduced himself to the Contessa, who gave him the key of a spare room in her suite. The replacement for the dead wireless operator had established himself.

Four days later he passed on a message to the Contessa, who relayed it to Aldo. On a bright Sunday morning, Aldo, wearing his best suit and having attended Mass, entered an inn in the crowded working-class district of the town. In the back room six men were playing cards and drinking the local vintage. Workers by day, they were Partisans by night, but to the outside world they were just a bunch of jovial workers, happily passing the little spare time they had from the factory.

Aldo's entry gave them the opportunity to make some light-hearted cracks at the boy's expense. Aldo took it all in good part.

"A glass of wine, Aldo?"

"Yes, please."

"My, my," came the sarcastic but true remark, as the wine was poured out, "some of our lads seem to have become men since the war."

"And how's that so-and-so Fascist Contessa of yours?"

"Now, now," said the sarcastic one, "you shouldn't be rude about a lady who was decorated, not only by the King, but by the great Mussolini himself."

"That was for the work in the hospitals in the First World War, and for her charity," was Aldo's furious defense.

"Don't let them annoy you, Aldo. It's just a bit of fun. Now tell us why you're here. We haven't seen you lately."

"The wireless operator has been replaced . . ."

"Let's hope he'll be more prudent than the last," murmured one of the men.

"And a message has come through," added Aldo.

It was a cardinal point with these men never to ask who had received the message, and who was really the head one guiding the activities of these Partisans. So far, Aldo had never let them down.

"The message asks us to blow up the railway viaduct to the north of the town, otherwise the British and American Air Forces will do it. They don't want to bomb it because if we do it, it may save unnecessary loss of lives among our people. They give us six days."

"And with what shall we do it?" asked one man angrily, "our knives and forks?"

"We haven't enough explosives to blow up a pussy cat," said another.

"Then I must leave the laundry for you tomorrow, Giuseppe," said Aldo. "What time will you be home?"

"I'm on the early shift tomorrow," said Giuseppe. "Come any time after five o'clock."

With the Contessa's permission, it was a weekly chore for Aldo to deliver the laundry that his mother did for a special clientele.

He wheeled his handcart to his first customer, Father Pietro. The priest kindly asked the boy in to share a pot of wartime coffee with him.

When the boy left, his handcart was appreciably heavier.

Aldo's next call was to Giuseppe, and he pushed his cart along at a smart pace, since any nosy Nazi trying to be important might quite easily ask him to empty his load, just for fun.

Giuseppe was home. Aldo took his cart inside, and when the boy said "*Addio, Giuseppe,* " the cart was considerably lighter. He had left a large quantity of explosive material with the Partisan. Four nights later the viaduct had been dynamited. Railway traffic was disrupted for eight months.

The Nazi commandant of the district was furious. He issued an order that should there be a recurrence of such sabotage, a hundred hostages, men, women, and children, would be taken and shot. And he meant it. It had become a common form of retaliation in Nazi-occupied countries.

Confirmation of this brutal order came about in a strange way. The commandant had telephoned the Contessa, asking if he might call on her.

"I would be delighted," replied the Contessa. "Have tea with me tomorrow at four o'clock. But—being a German, your tea will be coffee, and a real, good one."

Punctually, as the clock struck four, the German commandant

was shown into the Contessa's salon. He clicked his heels and bowed low over her welcoming outstretched hand.

"It is kind of you, Madam, to receive me."

"Not at all, General, I am delighted that you have found the time to call on me. It is a long time since we have met . . ."

"Not since we took over your palace."

"And I see so few worthwhile people here," continued the Contessa. "I am shunned by the Parmensi. The people of Parma don't like my politics, but there it is. We are just as God made us."

They were interrupted by the arrival of Luigi, accompanied by two waiters, who brought in a feast to satisfy a dozen Germans.

"You should not have gone to all this trouble," murmured the commandant.

"It isn't every day that I entertain so exalted a personage," said the Contessa.

"Tell me," continued the Contessa, "are you really serious about the proclamation you have issued concerning sabotage and hostages? Or is it to frighten the saboteurs?"

"Quite serious, Contessa. I have done it on the orders of the field marshal."

"And how is the dear field marshal? We met in Rome some years ago."

"He is well, but somewhat worried at the moment. I can tell you, in confidence, because you are one of us, heart and soul, that the Allied landing in Sicily is viewed with some gravity."

The general was interrupted by the telephone bell. The Contessa answered it.

"Excuse me—it is for you, General."

Evidently, from the way he received the message it was something serious.

"Yes, yes, see that the line to the field marshal is clear. I will be back in good time."

In a more lighthearted manner he continued the conversation with the Contessa.

"Now, where was I? Oh yes, Sicily. There is always the possibility that if the enemy invade Italy proper and move northward, the Italians will crumple and sue for peace. You must pardon me, Contessa, when I say that I do not trust the Italians. But whatever happens, we shall continue the fight until we achieve final victory.

"But I have not called on you to tell you that. The field marshal instructed me to make this visit. If we move northward we shall have to take charge of a number of prisoner-of-war camps. We will, of course, close them, and transfer the prisoners to Germany. We have a camp not very far from here, and the field marshal has come up with a brilliant idea.

"Most prisoners have been in the camp for a considerable period. Many of them are Irish. I see that you smile, Contessa. We know that you are Irish . . ."

"No, General, Italian."

"Quite, Contessa, but you had an Irish father and an Irish mother. You must have Irish sympathies, and you Irish are very clannish. The field marshal's idea is that you speak to the prisoners, particularly the Irish, and explain our point of view to them. Instead of rotting in camp, they can join us and fight on the winning side."

"But surely, a small number of men . . ." protested the Contessa.

"It is not the number, but the effect on the morale of the troops. Imagine, if a number of Allied men and officers were to desert . . . incidentally, the senior British officer is an Irishman, Colonel O'N——. Surely the Irish have no love for the British."

"A brilliant idea," conceded the Contessa, "please congratulate the field marshal."

"I will, when I speak to him this evening. Then I will make the arrangements for you to visit the camp. We are sure that you will succeed."

An hour later, after the commandant had left, Luigi came to see that everything had been satisfactory.

"Did you listen to the phone message for the commandant?" asked the Contessa.

"But certainly," replied Luigi, "and our GHQ already have it. The HG—the Hermann Goering Division—is being moved from the Brenner Pass to central Italy."

Twelve hours later an Anglo-American air force with its heavy bombers created havoc in the division.

The sentries saluted as the Contessa, accompanied by Aldo, and driven by an officer of the prison camp, entered the gate.

The Contessa was received by Captain C——, commanding officer of the camp, who looked askance at Aldo.

"You must excuse me bringing my servant with me, but I am liable to heart spasms at any moment and he knows what to do."

The captain led them to his office, where he introduced the Contessa to Colonel O'N——. Also in the room was an Italian lieutenant. It was the Contessa's turn to be surprised.

"This is an English-speaking officer who must be present at your interview," explained the captain.

"But nothing of this was said to me by the German commandant," retorted the Contessa.

"In the absence of any instructions," said the captain, "I must do this."

"Very well," answered the Contessa with polite resignation.

She and Colonel O'N—— faced one another across the table. As she sat down, she whispered, "Don't believe a word I say about Nazi victories."

"Please speak up," interrupted the Italian officer. "No whispering, please."

The Contessa gave him a beaming smile.

"You speak English very well."

"I should. I spent many years in England."

"Which Italian hasn't?" said the Contessa, and even the solemn British colonel laughed.

Aldo did not smile. His eyes were riveted on his mistress, waiting for his cue, if it came.

"I don't know if you have been informed of the reason for my visit—"

"I can guess," interrupted the colonel.

"So my reputation has obviously reached this camp," continued the Contessa. "As you know, the Allies have landed in Sicily, and will doubtless invade Italy. If they move northward, your *dolce vita* in this camp will be over. You will all be transferred to Germany. . . . Now, it has occurred to the German Staff that many of you, especially the Irish prisoners—and, being Irish myself, I know that they have little love for the British—would prefer to side with the Germans and be on the winning side rather than rot in a German prison camp."

One look at the colonel's face was answer enough.

"Madam, save your breath, if you have come—"

But he got no further. The Contessa clutched at her heart. It was Aldo's cue. He sprang up and in an agonized voice demanded a glass of water from the Italian lieutenant, who ran out of the room to get it. The Contessa recovered amazingly, while Aldo kept watch at the door.

"Quick," she said, "we have only a few moments. I am on your side. We must play for time."

"How do I know that you are on the level?"

"Do you listen to the BBC?" asked the Contessa.

"Perhaps we do," came the guarded reply.

"Then give me a message or a line you are fond of, and I will have it relayed to you."

"Very well," said the colonel, "I'll chance it. 'It is love that I am seeking for, but of a beautiful, unheard-of kind.' "

"Won't you finish the quotation from Yeats?" asked the Contessa. "I will do it for you—'that is not in the world.' "

The colonel smiled and the Contessa felt a little happier.

A warning cough from Aldo put an end to the conversation, and he offered the Contessa a pill—pure peppermint—while the Italian officer gave her a glass of water, which she sipped very carefully.

Aldo took this opportunity to vanish from the room. Nobody noticed his going. He asked the first Italian soldier he saw where he could find Carlo? The soldier laughed.

"Which Carlo? We have a dozen of them."

"Carlo Marino of Parma," replied Aldo.

"You will find him doing sentry duty by the last block, over there."

Carlo was overjoyed to see Aldo. It was two months since he had been home, and news from a neighbor was very welcome. Aldo explained how he came to the camp.

"How are Mamma and my fiancée, Emilia?" asked Carlo.

"They are well," replied Aldo, "but very sad. You see, Carlo, you are not only on the list of the Garibaldini, but also on the Gappist's list, and you know what that means if these fighting Partisans get hold of you."

Carlo went white with fear.

"*Mamma mia!*" he gasped. "But what can I do?"

"I will try to help you," comforted Aldo. "I will tell them that you are kind to the prisoners, that is if you are kind to them. Are you on guard now?"

"This is the punishment block," said Carlo.

"How many prisoners are you guarding?"

"Only two. They tried to escape."

"And what is that building there?"

"That is the Generator Room where we make our own electricity, and next to it is the storeroom and the armory for ammunition and rifles and so on. But why am I telling you this? It can be of no interest to you."

"None at all," agreed Aldo. "I hope that you are well protected against any Partisan attack."

"Very well," said Carlo. "You see that double wire barrier inside the high walls? That is highly charged with electricity, and anybody touching it would be electrocuted."

"You don't say"—Aldo was suitably impressed. "I'm glad that you are so well protected. When I arrive home, I will give your love to your mother and to Emilia, and I will speak for you to the Partisans."

"Thank you, Aldo, you are a good friend."

"I think that I have made progress," said the Contessa, phoning the commandant. "But I would be grateful if you would ask Captain C—— not to have an Italian officer in the room when I speak to Colonel O'N——. It inhibits him from speaking frankly. . . . Thank you, General. In a few days the colonel must speak to one or two of the senior officers and sound them out. . . . Thank you. I will phone Captain C—— for transportation."

Five days elapsed before the colonel's choice from the Irish poet, W.B. Yeats, was broadcast. It was repeated twice, and at the end of the quotation came an addition—"She's OK, Colonel."

On her next visit to the camp, the Contessa was allowed to be alone with the colonel, while Aldo spent his time with Carlo, who was off duty, and who did his best to impress Aldo with his kindness to the prisoners, and to act as a guide around the camp.

The success of the Allies in Southern Italy meant that a plan for an escape for all the prisoners had to be perfected without delay.

The first step was that the Contessa asked and was given permission to address the prisoners. Only the senior officers knew the true situation. The men were allowed to be as rude and as vocal as servicemen can be.

Now and again a senior officer would call for "fair play for the lady," even though they might disagree with, and dislike what she was saying.

Again, the Contessa gladdened the heart of the Nazi commandant with a report of progress. She was sure that after her next visit she would have a list of names of the men who would come over to the Nazi side.

The Contessa held a council of war with Aldo and Luigi. It was decided that she would pay a visit to her doctor in Milan, taking Aldo with her, while Luigi would spend his day off in Bologna, meeting some old friends.

On her return from Milan, obviously having derived considerable benefit from her visit to the doctor, the Contessa went once again to the prisoner-of-war camp. The manner in which Captain C——received her was evidence of the esteem in which she was held by the Nazi High Command. Even Aldo was given the free run of the camp, while the Contessa perfected her plan with Colonel O'N——, who handed her a list of names, including an officer and several noncommissioned officers, willing to desert to the other side.

There was no heading to the list, and it might have been a duty roster of any description. But the main thing was accomplished. A D-day and a zero hour were agreed upon by the Contessa and the colonel. She now had his complete confidence.

"You, Aldo," ordered the Contessa, "will leave tomorrow morning at six, in Arturo Borelli's truck. Your first call will be to Teresa. She must warn all her peasant friends to be ready. Remember, Aldo, we have only two days in which to make sure that there will be no hitch. Then when you arrive at the Partisan headquarters, you know what to do. To you, Luigi, I leave the transport and uniform problems. Any failure there will be fatal. The rest I will take care of. Good luck, and *arrivederci*."

❋

The hours passed slowly until the time came for the Contessa to phone the Nazi commandant.

"General, we have been successful. Tell the field marshal that his plan has succeeded beyond our wildest dreams. We have a list of men who are willing to serve the Third Reich—yes, General, quite a number—oh, that's very kind and gallant of you, General, but it was your idea. Now, I have a suggestion to make. We must celebrate, and I would be delighted if you would honor me with your company and dine with me tonight. I won't take no for an answer. Shall we make it seven o'clock? . . . Oh no, General, the pleasure is mine."

A short conference with Luigi followed this conversation.

With Teutonic punctuality, on the stroke of seven the Nazi commandant once more clicked his heels and bowed low over the Contessa's outstretched hand.

"So charming of you to invite me, Contessa, to celebrate a notable victory. Knowing something of the British and the Irish, I appreciate that it was not easy."

Laughingly the Contessa agreed.

"But the word impossible is not in our vocabulary. Will you take sherry or port, or would you prefer an Italian aperitif?"

"Sherry, please."

The glasses were filled.

"To victory," said the Contessa.

As they raised their glasses to their lips, the door was unceremoniously thrown open, and four armed men entered. Two guns covered the general, and two were leveled at the Contessa. The black trench coat each man wore heightened his sinister appearance.

The door was locked on the inside.

The Contessa was the first to recover from the initial shock.

"What is the meaning of this outrage? How dare you—"

"Silence," hissed the leader of the malignant quartet.

The general was almost apoplectic.

"You will pay for this—"

"Silence, both of you," said the leader, "and sit down. Finish your drinks if you like, because it will be the last you'll have." He made a dramatic pause. "You are both under arrest."

"Are you mad?" stormed the general. "Do you know who I am, and who this lady is?"

"It is because you are both who you are," came the reply, "that you are under arrest. We are from the Special Branch of the Gestapo."

"When the field marshal hears—"

"We don't take our orders from the field marshal. We take ours from His Excellency Heinrich Himmler. But enough of talking."

The general was trying hard to control himself.

"On what charge are we under arrest?"

"You should know that well enough," sneered the leader. "You have both plotted for a mass escape tonight from a prisoner-of-war camp."

"That is ridiculous nonsense," came the indignant reply from the Contessa. "On the contrary—"

"Shut up," barked the Gestapo leader. "Our Intelligence has been aware of every move. If you wish to save your life, General— for the time being, at any rate—you will read this order to Captain C—— at the prisoner-of-war camp."

From his pocket he took out a sheet of paper, which he handed to the general.

"I will do no such thing," blustered the general, "whatever it is."

"You can please yourself," replied the leader, "but if I read it, you will not hear it, because you will be dead. Hermann"— this to one of his men—"get Captain C—— on the phone. Adolf, take up your position."

Adolf stood behind the general, with the muzzle of the gun pressed against his head.

"Captain C—— on the phone," said Hermann.

"Hand it over to the general." This was done. "Now read it, General, clearly, please."

The general sat at the table with the sheet of paper before him and the gun behind him. He read from the paper.

"Is that you, Captain C——? This is the commandant. What I am going to say to you is absolutely confidential. It is for you alone. Not a word of it must be said to anyone. You understand, not to anyone.

"The Gestapo and the High Command have uncovered a plot for

a mass escape from your camp tonight. There is no doubt that you have a traitor or traitors among your men. But that we will deal with later. This is what you have to do. You will have all your men, all armed, ready on the parade ground at twenty-one hours. At that time a company of SS men will arrive at the camp, under the command of Gruppenführer S——. He will take charge, and you will obey his orders. Not a word of this must reach your men or any of the prisoners. They must be allowed to believe that everything is normal. Is that understood? Heil Hitler!"

The general wiped the perspiration from his brow.

"Good," said the leader. "Now Hermann and Adolf, you will take the general to headquarters. Take the lift to the basement. The car is at the back entrance. And if there is any nonsense, shoot to kill."

"And what about the lady?" asked Hermann.

"I will interrogate the woman here, and then it will be Ravensbrück or Belsén."

As the general was led out, the Contessa collapsed into her chair, and covered her face with her trembling hands.

Promptly at twenty-one hours, two trucks crowded with Nazi SS men, and led by a Mercedes sedan, drove up to the gates of the prison camp. The Italian sentries were replaced by SS men, and were taken into the camp with the Nazi soldiers.

The Italian officers and men, everyone armed, were lined up on the parade ground, as Gruppenführer S—— stepped out of his Mercedes to be welcomed by Captain C——.

The SS men, each carrying a gun, quickly surrounded the Italians.

The Nazi officer pointed to six men on a platform, who manned the searchlights and the machine guns.

"Bring those men down."

Captain C—— obeyed, and six SS men replaced the Italians.

"Now order all your men to ground arms. Every weapon and all ammunition are to be placed on the ground."

Once again the scared captain gave the orders, which were promptly carried out.

"Now order your men to get into that truck. They are to be taken to headquarters. It will be a tight squeeze, but it won't do any of you any harm after the soft life you have had here. You, Captain, had better lead the way. Quickly, if you please."

Within four minutes the truck carrying the unarmed Italian officers and men, and six armed SS men, drove out of the camp on its way to headquarters.

As soon as the truck had left the camp, Aldo, who had been lying on the floor of the Mercedes, jumped out of the car.

The Gruppenführer was shaking with suppressed laughter, as his men collected the arms and ammunition from the parade ground.

"Well, Aldo," he asked, "how did I play my part?"

"I could only hear you, Andrea," replied Aldo. "You were magnificent."

"And don't our Partisans look the real thing as SS Nazi swine?"

"Wonderful, but we must hurry."

"Carry on, Aldo," said the Partisan, dressed as the Gruppenführer.

Swift as lightning the boy ran to the first hut and rapped on the door. Out of the hut stepped Colonel O'N——, followed by three of his senior officers.

Aldo introduced the colonel to the happy "Gruppenführer."

From the other huts streamed officers and men. A Guards' Regimental Sergeant Major took charge, and to an admiring crowd of "SS men" looking on, the men in their platoons stood to attention, as though they were Trooping the Color on Horse Guards Parade.

The colonel gave the order to stand "at ease." He addressed them.

"Those of you in Company A who are making a bolt for it will find all sorts of transport ready for you at the rear of the camp. Move quickly and silently. Four different routes are being taken to the Swiss border. The peasants and Partisans will find clothing and shelter for you. Good luck to you all."

"Same to you, sir," came the murmured response from the men.

"Carry on, Captain Wood."

The colonel took the salute as, to a muted *Colonel Bogey* on a mouth organ, the men marched out of the camp, looking hopefully to freedom.

"The rest of you," said Colonel O'N—— to the remainder of the men, "who are going with me to the Partisans, will fill the trucks that are waiting for you outside the camp. What is it, Aldo?"

Aldo had been tugging at the colonel's sleeve.

"Destroy telephone and wireless," whispered Aldo.

"Fall out, the Sappers," ordered the colonel.

Six men of the Royal Engineers fell out, and with Aldo leading them, it took exactly five minutes to cut off all possible communication with the outside world.

The men moved off to their trucks, and the parade ground was clear except for the Mercedes car. Aldo, carrying a sack, faced the colonel.

"What next, Aldo?"

Aldo reported that with the help of "SS" men he had ransacked the armory—not a gun or bullet was left—and that they had cleared the storeroom.

"Only the generator left," said Aldo, with a big grin.

Colonel O'N—— turned to his three brother officers, an Australian, a New Zealander, a Pole, and to the "Gruppenführer."

"I think that we can manage that ourselves."

Aldo, carrying the sack, led the way. The door of the Generator Room was open, and one large window had been smashed. Aldo handed each man a large hand grenade.

"As soon as we've lobbed them in there," said the colonel, "we run for shelter behind this punishment block. You go there now, Aldo."

In no time, with a big explosion, the Generator Room had ceased to exist.

The men and Aldo made their way across the dark parade ground to the glow from the headlights of the Mercedes.

The Contessa, in the happiest of moods, the two "Gestapo men," and Luigi were busy compiling a list of what the Partisans needed for the next Allied airdrop. They were interrupted by a knock on the door.

The men jumped up, drew their revolvers, and covered the entrance.

"Who is it?" asked the Contessa.

"Me, Contessa, Aldo," came the reply.

The door was quickly unlocked and in trooped Aldo, followed by the "Gruppenführer."

"Aldo." The Contessa held out welcoming arms. He ran to her

and she held him closely. For the first time in her long association with Aldo, the Contessa exhibited emotion.

The "Gruppenführer" and the "Gestapo men" hugged and congratulated one another.

Twelve hours later, twenty-four Italian soldiers, onetime prisoner-of-war guards, clad only in vests and pants, were released in the foothills of the Apennines to find their way home as best they could. The rest of their comrades had gladly joined the Partisans.

On the eighth of September, 1943 at 5:30 p.m., the Contessa, Aldo, and Luigi were grouped around the radio. Marshal Badoglio was to make an important announcement.

On the table was a bottle of the Contessa's best champagne, cooling in a bucket. The marshal spoke:

"The Italian Government recognizes the impossibility of continuing the unequal struggle against a superior foe and has, with a view to sparing the people further grave misfortune, requested General Eisenhower, Supreme Commander of the Anglo-American Forces, for an armistice. The request has been granted.

"In consequence of this, all hostile action against Anglo-American Forces by Italian Forces is to cease everywhere. The latter will, however, react against any attacks from another source."

The bottle of champagne was opened. The glasses were filled. The Contessa proposed a toast: "To Aldo, and to the Italy in which he hopes to live."

MR. CHURCHILL WANTS
TO KNOW

"You must get out of Oslo, immediately."

"Can't I hide until it all blows over?" pleaded fifteen-year-old Olav.

"You don't seem to realize," came the stern reply from Sven, "that half the Gestapo in Oslo, to say nothing of the police, are combing the city for somebody who answers your description. This isn't going to blow over."

This dialogue took place between the leader of a Youth Resistance Group and one of its members.

The previous night, Olav, with three other members of the Group, had prepared an "illegal newspaper" for distribution. They had "borrowed," with full permission of the owner, the flat of a sympathizer, who had gone to Bergen on business for a few days, and who had a cast-iron alibi, if anything went wrong.

Part of the flat was used as an office, and the four members of the Group, which included one expert girl typist, had typed, stenciled, and copied three hundred newspapers for distribution at important centers.

To avoid being out during the curfew, Olav, who had farthest to go, left early, carrying a neatly wrapped bundle in his school satchel.

As he gently closed the door of the flat in the dimly lit corridor, a gun was pressed into his back.

"Turn around and drop that satchel." It was the next-door neighbor. His door was slightly ajar. "Not for the first time I've heard typing and voices," he hissed, "when my neighbor has been away. You're going to make a nice prize for the Gestapo with that bundle of papers. I told you to drop that satchel; then put your hands up and walk through that door, the one that's open."

It is said that at the moment of drowning, a person's past life flashes before him. With Olav it was the reverse. At the moment of dropping his satchel, his whole future flashed before him. He saw the headlines in the news sheet he had just helped to prepare.

NO NORWEGIAN IS FOR SALE
BOYCOTT ALL SPORTING EVENTS. DON'T PLAY AND DON'T WATCH REFUSE TO BECOME NAZIS OR QUISLINGS
REMEMBER YOUR TRADE UNION LEADERS VIGGO HANSTEEN AND ROLF WICKSTRÖM, SHOT IN COLD BLOOD
DON'T VOLUNTEER TO FIGHT AGAINST THE RUSSIANS

It all added up to torture and death.

"If I am to die," he said to himself, "why not die fighting?"

Just as the satchel hit the ground, Olav flung himself on this foxy-faced man. The impact bore the man to the ground with Olav on top of him. The boy grasped the gun, and fought to wrest it from the man's grip. The struggle was fierce. Suddenly there was the muffled sound of a shot and the man lay still.

Olav sprang to his feet, picked up his satchel, rapped the arranged signal on the door of the flat, and entered just as the last of the Group was leaving by the fire escape.

Olav made no mention of the incident when he arrived home, having delivered the leaflets to their proper destination.

His parents were of good Norwegian stock. If his mother knew anything of his Resistance activity she made no mention or comment about it. His father was headmaster of a school in Oslo, and was well aware of Olav's membership of the Youth Resistance

Group. It was what he expected of his son, and there was no doubt where the father's sympathies lay.

The father was proud of both his sons. Henrik, eight years Olav's senior, was an officer in the Merchant Navy. When war was declared, the tanker in which he served entered a British port. It was of great service to the Allies and, so far, Henrik had been lucky.

Both sons exemplified the father's favorite dictum, "A sound mind in a sound body." Both might well be described as athletic scholars. It was only now and again that he cautioned Olav about the hot-tempered impulsive streak he had, an unusual trait in this phlegmatic Norwegian family.

"It is too late to cry over spilled milk," said Sven gently, "but if you had only picked up the gun, instead of leaving a clear set of fingerprints on it, you would have saved us a lot of trouble."

"I didn't think of it," murmured Olav apologetically. "I suppose I panicked a bit."

"Our contact at the hospital," continued Sven, "tells us that, before they operated, the man recovered consciousness sufficiently to whisper an excellent description of you. He is, or maybe by now was, an important Quisling and a valuable informer for the Nazis. The charge against you may be murder, but they've got enough against you, in any case, for the Gestapo to take you to their HQ in Victoria Terrasse and to torture you. They've had a dozen suspects there already, but the fingerprints did not tally."

"I wouldn't tell them anything," muttered Olav.

"That's what you think," replied Sven kindly. "That's what everybody thinks. But, alas, some do break down. They will comb the schools. So we have decided that you've got to get out of Oslo for all our sakes. We can arrange a quiet trip to Sweden."

"No, no, I don't want to hibernate in Sweden." Olav was indignant and emphatic in his refusal. "What good can I do there?"

"Don't be under any misapprehension that our co-workers in Sweden are idle. There would be plenty to do."

"No, please, not Sweden. I want to do something positive. Since the radios were confiscated last September, our secret newspapers are more important than ever. It's eighteen months since the Nazis occupied our country, and our resistance is mostly passive. Nor is it fun any longer to cut off the hair of girls who go out with German soldiers, or to spit when you see a Nazi soldier, even if you are fined for it. That's all kid's play."

"I know what you mean," interrupted Sven, "you've made your point. We guessed that Sweden might not appeal to you, so we've arranged for you to go to Trondheim. There's a suggestion that you dye your hair black."

"Oh no!" burst out Olav. "There's no sense in that. Fair hair and blue eyes is the commonest description of any Norwegian, but with black hair I could draw attention to myself."

"Once again you've made your point," admitted Sven. "Now listen carefully. You are going to be enrolled in the Technical High School in Trondheim. This is the name of the man you will report to at the school." He gave Olav a name, Mr. G——, and made him repeat it several times.

"I will explain to your teacher that you have left your present school. He will understand. You will catch the afternoon train from the East Station to Trondheim, without going home to say good-bye. I will do all that for you. I will see your father at his school, and your mother at home. I will bring you a packed bag from your home. You will travel with the guard. You will be his assistant, and will lodge in his home, unless Mr. G—— makes other arrangements for you. You may think that we're overcautious, but we cannot afford the minutest gamble. Too many lives are involved. Naturally, you will write to your parents, telling them how lucky you to have been chosen to go to the Technical High School, and that you have no complaints about anything. Remember that mail is often opened, and phones are tapped. Our contacts will keep us informed of your progress. And now, spend the next hour with our bookshop friend in Karl Johans Gate, learning something of Trondheim. Be at the station at a quarter to four. Here's your ticket. Report to the guard of the train. Say to him, 'They tell me you are fond of Ibsen.' He should reply, 'He was a good Norwegian.' If there is a change of guard and one of our men is off duty, you must take your chance as an ordinary passenger. In that case, report to Mr. G—— at the Technical High School when you arrive in Trondheim. One last word, Olav. Remember that although ninety-eight percent of the people of our country are on our side, the two percent of Quislings and rats are waiting and watching for us to be rash and to make a mistake."

"Would you ask my mother to come to the station?" asked Olav.

"Listen, Olav, mothers don't come to stations to say good-bye to train guards or their assistants. I will say good-bye for you."

Olav was relieved that the right guard was on the train.

"Just put on that uniform and look busy with those parcels, while I wait outside the van." But Olav was worried. Five minutes to go and no sign of Sven. Then, with two minutes to go, Sven arrived at the guard's van, carrying a suitcase which he handed to Olav, without a word, much to the boy's disappointment, because he rather liked the way he looked in the uniform. Sven also gave Olav an envelope, then turned on his heel and became lost in the hurrying crowd.

Meanwhile, Gestapo men, SS and police were checking passengers. Olav, the guard, and Sven breathed more freely when the train to Trondheim pulled out of the station. Olav opened the envelope on which his mother had written "With love." In it was a fifty-kroner note.

Once the train had gathered speed, the guard settled down for a chat with Olav. First he opened a packet of sandwiches, which he invited Olav to share with him.

"My name's Andreas. If it embarrasses you, you can say Uncle Andreas. You will lodge with my wife and myself, that is, if you would like to. We have no children of our own, so my wife is sure to make a fuss of you. As I often have to spend the night in Oslo, you will be fine company for her. Naturally, she knows nothing of the Resistance movement. She hates the Nazis and the Quislings, but that's because she's a good Norwegian. You are a student, who has come for further education to Trondheim Technical High School, and I am a friend of your parents, who have entrusted you to my care."

"Thank you, Uncle Andreas, I'm very grateful."

Andreas had not exaggerated when he said that his wife would make a fuss of Olav. A stout, motherly person, and a splendid cook, she lavished all her affection on this well-brought-up student.

On Andreas' advice, on his first day in Trondheim (to which city he was a stranger), Olav acquainted himself with Norway's third largest city.

On his second day in Trondheim, Olav reported to Mr. G—— at the Technical High School. Tall and spare, he could have been mistaken for a diplomat. He had a kindly, compelling personality, as pupils of the school for over thirty years could testify.

"I've been expecting you, Olav. Welcome to Trondheim. Let's take a walk in the grounds. It's a nice day, and it will give us some exercise."

Once in the open air, the teacher explained his tactics.

"I'm tired of searching for hidden microphones, so God's fresh air appeals to me. As you can guess, I am over military age, and as you are under military age, we should make a good pair. You will take a quick course as a shipbuilding apprentice, just to make you familiar with various tools. Then you will be transferred to a shipbuilding yard as an apprentice, attached to Oscar, one of the skilled workmen—a very fine fellow. Meanwhile, you and some of your classmates are members of the Quisling Youth Organization. Your papers are all in order. This afternoon, at three o'clock, you will report to me at the Sports Ground. Ask the porter to direct you. I know that there is a sports boycott, but that makes it ideal for our little group—good, honest Quislings that we are"—and he chuckled joyfully—"to meet in the open air, all above suspicion."

At three o'clock, Olav was introduced to Paul, Anders, Marius, Johan and Arne, all about his own age, and to three attractive sixteen-year-old girls, Margit, Hedda and Cornelia. They were all dressed for outdoor athletics, and to any curious observer, Mr. G—— was timing their performances.

"This Saturday, Marius," ordered the master, "I want you to take Olav to Erik's farm. In your spare time, Olav, if you have any, and on other special occasions, you will help on Erik's farm, and so win the approbation of the authorities."

The smiles of those present led Olav to believe that there was more to it than just helping on a farm. That Saturday he was introduced to Erik, his wife, and to Victor, the farmer's help and odd-job man, a dwarflike, middle-aged man, with a large appetite and a great sense of humor.

When Olav and Marius left to return to Trondheim, they carried with them sufficient food for some of the unfortunate Norwegians, who, for one reason or another, had been deprived of ration cards.

Olav made excellent progress at the school. He enjoyed the lessons, particularly the practical work, and was not yet called on to take part in Resistance activities.

"Don't be discouraged," Mr. G—— once said to him. "You will have plenty of opportunity in the near future, but I want you to attain a certain standard of proficiency in your work, or you may become suspect."

In the first week of January, 1942, Mr. G—— informed Olav that he was now a qualified apprentice and that he was to report to Oscar at the shipbuilding yard. He was given the necessary papers and a pass that admitted him to the yards and the dockyards.

"Since it is no secret that you are a member of the Quisling Youth Organization," warned Mr. G——, "you may have a rough time from some of the workmen. Of course, Oscar knows the truth, but neither he nor you will open your mouth. You will refuse to be drawn into any political discussion. Your stock answer will be, 'I'm too young to understand politics. I just want to do my work.' You will run across Marius and Anders, but don't be too chummy with them. Treat them as casual acquaintances. Obey Oscar implicitly, and if you are worried about anything seriously, you can always come to me."

Olav reported to Oscar and found him a genial giant. Well over six feet four and broad in proportion, he received Olav kindly and warned him to keep his eyes and ears open, but to keep his mouth shut. Olav also found comfort in Oscar's protective arm, which kept practical jokes against him harmless and down to a minimum.

In the middle of January, Olav received a message to report to Mr. G——.

"Let's take a walk around the grounds."

Once outside, Mr. G—— continued:

"I have sent for you, Olav, because I have a most important assignment for you, certainly the most important you have yet had. The German battleship *Tirpitz* is about to dock here in an hour or two. This is the Nazis' new and most powerful battleship. In fact, it is the most powerful one in the world. Our contacts in Great Britain tell us that it is the cause of much concern to Mr. Churchill. He had hoped that it could have been bombed during construction, but it wasn't." Mr. G—— smiled. "No, Olav, I don't expect you to bomb it. I wish you could. But Mr. Churchill wants to know every movement of the ship. Your work in the shipyard, and now and again in the dockyard, gives you good vantage points. You will hear gossip among the Nazi sailors. You will not be curious, because the Gestapo will be all over the place. Incidentally, you have been enrolled in extra evening classes here, so your coming and going will arouse no comment. But I don't expect to see you too often in the class, because, since your German is perfect, Oscar has arranged for you to help in the dockside tavern during much of your spare time, because you want to earn some extra money. That is where you may pick up the most valuable information through scraps of conversation and bits of gossip, because, when sailors have had a drink or two, the most innocent remark may be very significant. Above all, remember that the Gestapo will always be in the tavern, so don't be too curious to overhear a conversation, and watch out for their cunning tricks.

"Every scrap of information about the *Tirpitz* is tremendously important. Convoys carrying vital war material from Britain to Russia must pass north of our country. Warships try to protect them, but Mr. Churchill is worried about what might happen if the *Tirpitz* attacks. If he knows beforehand that the battleship is going to be there, he can make special arrangements. So you see, Olav, how important it is that we do not let Mr. Churchill down."

That night, Olav could not sleep. Through his brain kept drumming the refrain, "Mr. Churchill wants to know. We must not let him down." Churchill, who, alone, had defied the might of Germany! Olav vowed to himself that he would not let Mr. Churchill down.

Olav soon became quite expert at serving drinks to the sailors, who crowded into the dockside tavern. To his great surprise, one of the waitresses was Cornelia.

"Don't get hot under the collar," she warned Olav, "if the sailors make passes at me and try to be intimate. I can take care of myself, so never interfere, no matter what."

A group of sailors from the *Tirpitz* were in a particularly merry mood. Weren't they sailors on the most powerful battleship in the world? They were aching to have a go at the British convoys. Not a ship would escape them.

One of the sailors tried to date Cornelia. "How about coming to the cinema with me tomorrow?" he asked.

"Sorry," answered Cornelia, "but I'm not free until the end of the week."

"That's no good to me," laughed the sailor, "I'll be in the dark, icy Arctic by then."

"See you when you come back," smiled Cornelia.

At one of Olav's tables, the sailors were drinking plenty of *aqua vitae*.

"Drink, my little one," said one sailor to his mate. "You had better stoke up with good fiery stuff, because it's going to be very cold where we're going."

These bits of gossip earned much praise from Mr. G——.

"Just to keep your hand in," said Oscar to Olav one afternoon, "here's a little job for you. We are holding a big meeting of workers at the end of the day's work. You don't have to be there, and if I know anything about the Nazis they'll concentrate all their officers and Gestapo spies at the meeting. For example, the fuel tanks over there will be unguarded for some time. Now, with a good drill, a few holes could be bored. Carry a bag of tools, it is less suspicious. And wear a pair of old gloves—no fingerprints"—hardly a reminder that Olav needed.

As Oscar had predicted, all the German guards had been posted at the meeting where there was much wrangling about wages and rations.

Olav did his job well, and with obvious relish. The next morning an announcement was made that there had been serious sabotage of an oil tank, and, that when the culprit was caught, he would be summarily executed.

The *Tirpitz* had gone north, but there was still much to be gleaned in the tavern about other units of the German Navy, particularly U-boats. One evening, a customer in plain clothes became very chatty with Olav.

"You don't look the type to be a waiter in a place like this," he said. "You seem too intelligent."

"Thank you, sir," said Olav modestly, "but I need the extra money."

"What do you do otherwise?" asked the customer.

"I'm a shipbuilding apprentice. I'm trying hard to become a qualified workman."

"Did you see the *Tirpitz* when she was here the other day?"

"Oh, yes!"—and Olav's eyes shone with enthusiasm. "Isn't she a beautiful ship!"

The customer beckoned Olav to bend down, so that he could whisper to him. "But between you and me, wouldn't you like to blow it to bits?"

Olav shrank away, horrified.

"Oh, sir, how can you say a thing like that? I love ships."

"But you're one of us," persisted the customer. "You're a Norwegian."

"Of course I'm a Norwegian," responded Olav, "but to have such a horrible thought! You must be teasing me."

"By the way," continued the customer, "did you hear about the oil-tank sabotage?"

"Only what they broadcast, and the poster offer of twenty thousand kroner reward for information."

"Wouldn't you like a sum like that?"

"Who wouldn't?" laughed Olav.

"Because, between ourselves"—and again the man was confidential—"they say it was probably an apprentice, because all the men were at the meeting."

"You *are* pulling my leg," laughed Olav.

Cornelia had been watching this tête-à-tête between Olav and the man. She had no doubt that he was either from the Gestapo or an informer. She thought it was time to intervene. She strode over to the table and spoke angrily to Olav.

"Say, what's the idea? People are waiting for drinks, there's a pile of dishes to wash, and you stand here talking and talking."

"Sorry," muttered a contrite Olav as he streaked away.

"You must pardon me for interrupting," said Cornelia to the man, "but I hate lazy people. Can I get you anything, sir?"

"Nothing, Miss, thank you."

He rose and left.

✻

Bad news travels fast. Andreas returned from a journey to Oslo with the news that Olav's father had been arrested.

"I am going with you, Uncle Andreas, on your next journey to Oslo," said Olav.

"Not on your life," replied Andreas, with a determination that was entirely new to Olav. "The Gestapo have a complete dossier on your brother, Henrik. Your house and your mother are under constant observation. Any visitor to the house is suspect. I can fully appreciate your wish, Olav, but you are confusing courage with foolhardiness. Don't for one moment think that your mother doesn't know what you feel."

"But she is so alone," said Olav.

"No, Olav, she is not alone as long as Sven and your old group are free. One way and another, they manage to keep in touch with her. I want you to give me your word of honor that you won't go to Oslo. Too many lives may depend on it."

After a moment's hesitation, Olav murmured, "I promise."

"Thank you, Olav. I will bring you any news that there is."

The reason for the arrest of Olav's father was that twelve thousand out of the fourteen thousand teachers in Norway had openly rebelled against compulsorily enrolling the children in a Nazi Youth Movement, and against belonging themselves to a Nazi Teachers' Front. Arrests were made all over the country, and many were sent to the notorious concentration camp at Grini, a suburb of Oslo, where they were unmercifully tortured.

There was little Olav could do. His group in Trondheim contacted certain teachers who were still free, and asked them if they wanted to leave the country.

"Knowing the quality and the temper of the teachers," said Mr. G—— to his group, "they are likely to refuse, but if there are any who prefer to escape, explain that the sea journey to England is very hazardous at the moment, but our route to Sweden is at their disposal."

As Mr. G—— suspected, nearly all the teachers preferred open rebellion to escape. When the Gestapo and police came to arrest them, parents and children followed them to the railway station, cheering and shouting encouraging slogans. The children crowded around to give them cigarettes and food, but the SS dashed the gifts to the ground and threatened to shoot the crowd.

The climax came with the journey of five hundred teachers— among whom was Olav's father—to Trondheim, where they were to embark on an old wooden ship, the SS *Skjerstad,* built in 1904. Packed in unheated cattle cars, the teachers had no food and had to stand during a sixteen-hour journey. From the station at Trondheim, they were driven onto the old ship and packed into the hold, which could barely accommodate half the number.

Olav tried to get a glimpse of his father, but conditions made it impossible. The ship was due to sail within the hour, and during that period Mr. G—— tried a last desperate chance. Accompanied by Olav, he went too see D——, a Norwegian Nazi, a onetime neighbor of Mr. G——, who was in charge of the embarkation. He explained that if Olav could persuade his father to give in, many other teachers might follow, which would be a feather in D——'s cap.

The idea appealed to D——, and Olav's father was brought up from the hold and dumped onto a packing case. He was almost unrecognizable. Bent double with the blows he had received, this grand man looked practically subhuman.

"Let's go and have a drink while they talk," suggested Mr. G—— to D——. The offer was accepted with alacrity.

It took all Olav's willpower not to break down, as he sat beside his father on the packing case. Father and son clasped hands, and for a moment neither spoke for fear of weeping.

"How are you, Olav?"

"I'm fine, Father."

"This is a miracle. All the way to Trondheim, I kept wondering —would I get a glimpse of you? And here you are. You know, Olav, what was wonderful too? It was the children. In all the stations we went through, we heard the children on the platform, singing the national anthem, *Yes, We Love This Land,* and shouting encouragement to us. Wasn't that wonderful, Olav?"

"Yes, Father, it was wonderful. Father, I would like you to do something for me and for all the Resistance workers. We want all Norway, and all the world, to know what the teachers have been through. It must be a firsthand account, written by someone like yourself. Now, if you, Father, were to tell a white lie and to say that you have changed your mind, that you will join the Nazi Teachers' Front . . . "

"Say no more, Son. The men below look up to me. Whichever way you look at it, it would be desertion. What would the children think? It was to them we said, 'We teachers have been proud of you during the time our country has been occupied.' No, Olav, my son, thank you, but no. Now, tell me, how are you getting on with your studies?"

"Fine, Father, fine."

"Good. If you get a message back to your mother, tell her I am all right. Don't add to her distress."

Mr. G—— and D—— had returned to the ship. Olav shook his head sadly. Father and son were still clasping hands, but Olav was trembling all over.

"Good-bye, Father. We'll meet again soon."

"Of course we will, Son."

Two men picked up Olav's father, and dumped him back into the hold.

"Work slowly and work badly." That was the advice Oscar gave to Olav and to the workmates he could trust.

In the tavern, Olav learned that the teachers had been taken to Kirkenes.

"You can't help admiring them," said one Nazi sailor. "After all, they're only civilians, and to put up with the same treatment that the Russian prisoners get takes some doing."

"They're crazy not to join us," remarked another sailor. "They'll have to in the end."

"I don't know," said a doubter. "I don't like the news I hear from home." And with that, he had a quick look around the tavern, regretting his hasty comment.

The *Tirpitz* was anchored in Trondheim, and Cornelia soon discovered that the battleship was due to leave on the third of July, but she passed on the news to Olav, because, by now, the group took it for granted, in a kindly, humorous way, that there was a close link between the *Tirpitz,* Olav, and Mr. Churchill. In some inexplicable way, Olav felt that he was contributing to the ineffectiveness of the most powerful battleship in the world by keeping his promise to Mr. Churchill.

Trondheim was a thorn in the Nazi regime. The inhabitants, by their contempt and hatred for the Nazis and the Quislings, demonstrated that nothing and nobody could extinguish their love of freedom.

Time and again the Nazis were reminded of two cardinal points in the Norwegian Constitution—that no Norwegian can be imprisoned without a trial, and that there shall be unlicensed printing, and freedom of the press.

Even the children demonstrated their independence by scrawling or daubing HR (Haakon Rex), H7 (Haakon the Seventh), the "V" sign, or "Down with Quisling" on the walls or in public vehicles.

Mr. G—— had warned his Youth Group not to participate in these expressions of patriotism, because the punishment—torture or death for any grownup—was out of all proportion to the alleged crime. In any case, the Youth Resistance Group had enough to do. News had reached Mr. G—— from an official source that Josef Terboven, Norway's Nazi dictator, was planning a reign of terror in Trondheim, to teach the inhabitants a lesson. It was to begin in two days' time, on the sixth of October.

The names of certain suspects were given in confidence to Mr. G——. Members of the Youth Group contacted these people. Some were optimists and refused to believe the worst. The others, with false identity papers, were sent to peasants in the country, to Sweden, and to hideouts in Trondheim itself.

On the sixth of October, Terboven, with Police-General Rediess, drove through Trondheim in state, followed by police on motorcycles, with mounted machine guns. In addition, the Gestapo and the SS poured in from Oslo.

Thirty-four Norwegians were arrested and summarily sentenced to be executed. That evening, an announcement was broadcast of the execution of ten men. The condemned men heard of their own death, since they were not shot until the following morning. This same refinement of cruelty was adopted with the remaining twenty-four men. Terboven celebrated his first day's work by holding a party, while the SS and the Gestapo ransacked the homes of the murdered men. Terror reigned unabated. Home after home was searched. Hundreds of people were arrested, and beams of search-lights swept the streets, seeking any curfew breakers.

A local journalist, turned Quisling for a good purpose, tipped off Mr. G—— that there was to be a widespread search of local farms, ostensibly for hoarded food.

Three of the group—Johan, Arne, and Hedda—were rushed out to Erik's farm. Victor, who had just relayed abroad his account of the murders in Trondheim, speedily buried his wireless transmitter in the potato fields. By the time the Gestapo search party arrived, Erik's storeroom gave a very fair imitation of what Old Mother Hubbard's cupboard was like. After all, wasn't he a good farmer, who delivered 100 percent of his produce to the authorities?

Not a day or night passed without Olav thinking of the agony his father must be suffering in the far North. Soon there would be months without any sun, and the stories about the torture many of the teachers had to suffer gave him sleepless nights.

This particular day, his father had seemed closer to him than ever. It had ben a day of drudgery at work, made more unpleas-ant by two false-alarm air raids. The Nazis were becoming very jit-tery.

As he trudged home at the end of the day, he wondered why a message had been left for him at the tavern that he was expected home for dinner. He tried to throw off his gloomy mood as he entered the house.

"I'm so glad that you've come home," said Aunt Nora, Andreas' wife.

"I got your message at the tavern," said Olav. "But what's the great occasion?"

He pointed to the dining-room table, covered by a white lace cloth, on which stood two candles, a few flowers—something spe-cial in themselves—and the best dinner service.

"Is it somebody's birthday?"

"I don't know, Olav," interrupted Nora. "Andreas rang me this morning, before he left on the return journey from Oslo, and he said, 'Sweetheart, a gala dinner tonight, and ask Olav to be there. I will bring the food and drink!' That's all he said. I've tried to think of a reason. He always says 'gala dinner' when we celebrate a birthday or a wedding anniversary. Is it your birthday, Olav?"

"No, Aunt, not for months."

"Then we'll just have to wait and see." She looked at the clock. "It won't be very long now."

"I'd better go and wash, and put on my best suit," said Olav. "I can't sit down to a gala dinner in grimy overalls."

He had barely gone to his room when Andreas entered the house. He carried a bulging knapsack, which he put on the kitchen table. He was in a happy mood.

"Is Olav here?" This was his first question.

"Yes, he's upstairs, washing and changing."

"Good, then I'd better do the same."

Andreas left his wife to unpack the knapsack. There was cold meat, fish, cheese, butter, half a dozen eggs (an unbelievable sight), canned fruit, cream, cans of hors d'oeuvres, biscuits, bottles of beer, and many small delicacies. Nora could hardly believe her eyes. Instinctively she bolted the front door and put the chain on. Obviously it had all been smuggled in from Sweden, but by whom and for what reason?

When the three of them sat down to the candle-lit festive table, Olav found an envelope, with his name on it, propped against his glass.

"May I open it?" he asked.

"Of course," answered Andreas, and he kept his eyes on Olav as he read the letter.

Olav's hands began to tremble and there were tears in his eyes as he murmured, "My father's home, he has written to me. He came home this morning."

"I know," said Andreas gently.

"Did you see him, Uncle?"

"No, Olav, but I heard all about the crowds that suddenly seemed to come from nowhere, and the children that welcomed your father and the other teachers."

"Yes," said Olav, "he says so here. They sent many teachers back because there's chaos in the schools, and because these teachers are overage, except for teaching. Is that the reason for the gala dinner, Uncle Andreas?"

"Yes, Olav. It wasn't my idea. It originated with Sven and your old Resistance Group. When and how they smuggled all this from Sweden I don't know. But no letter, Olav. I will take them your thanks."

"Will you take a letter to my father, when you return to Oslo?"

"Yes, Olav, as long as there is no politics in it. We cannot be too careful."

Olav offered Andreas a fifty-kroner note.

"It is the note my mother gave me when I left Oslo. Will you please ask Sven, if he can possibly do it, to buy some flowers for my mother? She loves flowers. Now I'll go and write my letter."

As Olav left the room, two great tears rolled down the round cheeks of Aunt Nora.

"What are you crying for, my pet?" asked Andreas.

"I'm so happy for Olav."

The reverses of the German Army in Russia were bringing great comfort to the Norwegians, and many Quislings were beginning to regret their choice. Party badges were found in gutters, resignations were offered, but not accepted, and many fled to Sweden, ironically enough, as political refugees.

All these items of news, and the news transmitted from the Norwegian Government in London and from the BBC, had to be made known by means of illegal newspapers, and in this activity the Youth Group played a prominent part.

It was decided to issue a special edition when news came that the Oslo Central Labor Exchange had been burned down, thus destroying all the card indexes of the compulsory labor service. In their jubilation to make the news known, five members of the Trondheim group were nearly caught. Only the presence of mind of Hedda and Margit saved the day.

They were on duty outside a haberdashery shop, ostensibly window shopping. In the back room of the shop, the leaflets were being prepared. Hedda spotted an SS car coming in their direction. As it pulled up opposite the shop, she promptly fainted in the doorway, and Margit gave a fine exhibition of hysterics, warning the proprietor of impending danger and blocking the entrance to the shop. A small crowd had by now gathered there.

The proprietor relayed the warning, and within a minute the

back room was empty, leaving no trace of the group's activity. He then added more confusion by protesting at people fainting in the entrance of his shop, and voiced a further grievance when he discovered that the SS had come as a search party—and not as customers.

Naturally, nothing was found and Hedda recovered sufficiently to be led gently away by Margit.

An influx of sailors and dockyard experts necessitated the services of an additional waitress in the tavern, and Hedda was hired.

At the end of the third day, Olav, Cornelia, and Hedda pooled their harvest of rumors and gossip, and with the help of Mr. G—— the conclusion arrived at was that a specially constructed base for U-boats was being prepared in Trondheim Harbor. The sequel to the news gathered by the members of the Youth Resistance Group came six days later, when about midday there was an air-raid warning.

"Take cover," shouted the police and the Nazi soldiers, but the Norwegian workers in the shipyards and the dockyards, and the Norwegians in the streets, remained in their places and scanned the skies.

The sound of the plane engines became louder, the Nazis shrieked, "Take cover," but many of the Norwegians still did not budge.

Suddenly the planes became visible and the Norwegians waved to the pilots. It was really a futile gesture to planes so high above the ground, but it gave them much satisfaction.

Finally, they were literally driven into shelters, just as the American bombers dropped their loads and wrecked the work done by the Nazis, who hoped to create a wonderful U-boat base.

When the all clear sounded and Oscar and Olav emerged into the daylight, they laughingly shook hands.

And Olav said to himself, "Mr. Churchill certainly knew."

Much to Olav's regret, the *Tirpitz* was in the far North at Altenfiord, waiting to pounce on British convoys. Then came a day that Olav was never likely to forget. Mr. G—— sent for him, and he was somewhat surprised to see farmer Erik leaving Mr. G.——'s house.

"Sit down, Olav, and take a deep breath."

Mr. G—— was obviously in a good mood. "I've wonderful news for you. Two British midget two-men submarines penetrated the most strongly defended harbor of all time. They crossed a German minefield, and had to go fifty miles up the fiord to where the *Tirpitz* was anchored. They torpedoed the battleship. The explosions made it heave several feet out of the water. I thought you'd like to know."

The defeats of the Nazis in Europe were adding to the harassment and the embarrassment of the occupation troops and to the Quislings in Norway. Members of the Resistance Groups, especially in their help to Norwegian commandos, who were dropped by parachute, were becoming more daring, and in some cases more rash with their acts of sabotage.

So it came about that Marius and Johan were listed as "wanted men," and it took all the ingenuity of Andreas to smuggle them to Oslo, where Sven and his group took charge, and led them across the border to Sweden.

Once again the Nazis tried a call-up for compulsory Labor Service. But for the first time an Order of the Day was broadcast by the Norwegian Home Front from London. Olav, with the help of Oscar, made sure that the workers in the dockyards would know of it. The words from London came loud and clear. No one must obey the call-up. The success of the appeal can be judged by the fact that the Oslo Labor Exchange was again blown up, and in Trondheim, third largest city in Norway, one person answered the call-up.

It was General Eisenhower, Supreme Commander of the Allies, who now asked a service of the Norwegians. He wanted the transport of German troops to be hampered as much as possible, and what better way than by wrecking railway tracks. In one night a thousand men sabotaged a thousand points of the railway lines, from the north to the south, all the Youth Resistance Groups of the country making a substantial contribution.

News reached the Allies that the *Tirpitz* was ready to put to sea from Altenfiord, and once again the luckless ship was put out of action by dive-bombers from the *Victorious* and the *Furious.* Mr. G—— kept Olav informed of these actions and later told him that the *Tirpitz* had been moved to Tromso for repairs.

Relieved of watching the battleship for the time being, Olav concentrated on learning from Oscar what damage could result from a clumsy piece of welding, or from an ill-fitting screw. Then came a great day for Olav. Once again Mr. G—— sent for him, this time to Erik's farm. On the table were four glasses and a bottle of wine. Erik and Victor made up the quartet.

It was the twelfth of November, 1944. Never had Olav seen these three men so happy. Mr. G—— poured out the wine.

"I promised myself that I would open this bottle when the Germans left Norway, but today's news is so wonderful that I decided to open it; and I don't care, Olav, if you get drunk. Today, Lancasters of the Royal Air Force scored three hits on the *Tirpitz* with twelve-thousand-pound bombs. The battleship turned turtle. And your special assignment, Olav," added Mr. G——, "has come to a glorious end. Skoal! Let's drink to the Lancaster bombers."

They drank the toast. Then Olav put his timid question. "Does Mr. Churchill know already?"

"Yes, Olav, Mr. Churchill knows and he is most grateful."

BLOODY BUT UNBOWED

Spring in Bosnia in 1942. A perfect day. The sun shone from a cloudless blue sky, casting shadows on the green hills around the peasant's whitewashed house. The hum of bees came from the plum orchard which surrounded the house, and the air was scented with flowers. It was an ideal picture of peace, making incredible the horrible war that raged over Yugoslavia and the rest of Europe.

It was the perfect setting for the happy family that came from the house. They were to be photographed by three kind strangers who were passing by. The family, dressed in national costumes, were lined up against the wall of the house. Father and mother stood at either end, with four children—twin girls of six, and two boys one of ten and one of eight—between them. The three strangers faced them.

"A beautiful family group," remarked one of the men.

"But it is not complete," said the proud mother. "Peko, our eldest son—he is fourteen—has gone down into the village for the weekly groceries, such as we can get, and he will be back at any minute. Won't you wait for him?"

"I'm sorry, we can't do that. Now smile, and look happy because we want everybody to know how happy you Yugoslavs are."

It was at this moment that Peko, knapsack on back, having taken a shortcut up the mountain road, caught a first glimpse of his happy family outside the house. He heard the echo of the words "smile and look happy" and was just about to cry out, "Wait for me."

In that split second, the three men, facing his smiling family, took out Schmeisser submachine guns from beneath their coats, and mowed down his parents and his brothers and sisters.

Their bodies slumped to the ground and lay still. Then one of the men lit a firebrand and threw it into the house.

Peko was rooted to the spot. He could not believe his eyes. This must be a nightmare from which he would soon awake. But the words that reached him brought him back to reality.

"I could do with a nice glass of plum brandy. Let's go down into the village," said one of the men.

"We've earned it," said another laughingly.

The third man sprayed the dead bodies with bullets from his machine gun.

"Just a little extra for luck," he said.

Then the three murderers began their descent to the village below.

As soon as they had turned the corner, Peko, risking life and limb, left the mountain road and ran down the steep, almost precipitous side of the mountain, to rush to his house.

The house, now fully ablaze, was beyond saving, but it was to his family that he ran in case there might be a spark of life in one of them. But the Nazis had been very thorough. Peko's whole family had been wiped out. He was alone in the world.

He did not waste a moment commiserating with himself. Agile as a mountain goat, he ran up the road that was a shortcut to the village a mile and a half away.

Within ten minutes he spotted the three men, and heard them singing a merry German marching song.

Peko kept them in view until they entered Slavko's inn.

The boy waited outside for two or three minutes, trying hard to control himself.

Slavko was surprised to see him.

"Where have you been, you rascal?" asked the innkeeper. "I thought you were home an hour ago."

Then, suddenly, he noticed that something was wrong with Peko. The boy was trembling, and his high Slav cheekbones only accentuated the pallor beneath his normal brown, sunburned face. The usual twinkling eyes were sad and filled with tears.

"What's wrong, Peko? You look as if you'd seen a ghost."

"Three Nazis have just come in here?" asked Peko.

"Yes," answered Slavko. "They're in the back room, in a merry mood, drinking slivovitz"—and, under his breath, he added, "may it choke them."

In a few graphic sentences Peko described the massacre of his family. It was Slavko's turn to go white, for Peko's father had been his friend from boyhood.

"What do you want to do?" asked Slavko.

"I want to kill them," murmured the boy.

Slavko was not surprised.

"That's fair enough," he murmured. "You can do it. You're the best shot around here. Your father taught you to handle a gun when you were a lad of seven. I'll tell you what we'll do. When we come into the room, they'll probably stand up. You shoot the one on the right, I'll take the left one, and we'll both take the middle one. I'll get the guns."

Slavko returned with two loaded submachine guns.

"It's good there's no other customers here at the moment," whispered the innkeeper. "I'll put on the radio to cover some of the noise."

Slavko tuned in to Radio Belgrade, and the inevitable *Lili Marlene* blared out.

> *Unter der Laterne*
> *Vor dem grossen Tor* . . .

The men in the back room, somewhat tipsy with the strong liquor, sang the song with the radio.

Slavko flung open the door of the back room. The three Nazis, seeing the guns, sprang to their feet. Their own guns were on the table.

"You cursed Bosnian swine . . ." began one of them, but they were the last words he, or any of them, said. Within a minute Slavko and Peko had accounted for them.

❋

An hour's drive into a deep pine forest on the mountainside was the site selected by Slavko to bury the three murderers. He and Peko dug the graves themselves. They were the only two who would know what had happened to three Nazis, for these days it was hardly safe to trust anybody.

It was different, however, with the interment of Peko's family.

"We must give them a decent burial," said Slavko.

That evening at dusk, half a dozen close neighbors, headed by the priest, dug the graves by the ashes of their onetime home, and gave them a Christian burial.

"We won't mark the place," said the priest, "or the enemy may take out the bodies just for spite."

"I won't ever forget this piece of ground, father," said Peko, "and when the war is over, I will come back and put up a suitable memorial."

"What are you going to do, my son?" asked the priest.

"I am going to join the Partisans. I am alone in the world, so they must take me."

"Do you know where the nearest Partisans are?"

"I think so, father. About five or six miles up the mountainside."

"When you reach there, Peko, ask for Father Ribar. Tell him that I have sent you to him. Good-bye, Peko, my son, and may God bless and keep you."

Night had fallen, but fortunately it was full moon as Peko, following the mountain stream, had climbed for two hours in a series of loops, often winding round the edge of steep precipices.

Suddenly he came to a clearing. He remembered now that here was a Moslem village, where a year ago his father had taken him on a fishing trip. This might be an ideal place to spend the night. He walked across a green plain to the village. Not a sound or a sign of a human being was to be heard or seen. Some of the fruit was ripe on the trees. As he neared the ancient Mosque, he saw that the old houses and huts, huddled around the Mosque, were just burned-out shells. Everywhere was desolation. Lying on the ground outside one house was a fishing rod. Peko picked it up. Had it belonged to a boy like himself? Had the boy's father taught him to cast a fly, like his own father had done? Where were all the inhabitants? Had the Nazis marched them off to a concentration camp or to forced labor, or had they been massacred?

Peko decided that he would press on. This village of death was not the place in which to spend a night. He turned to go when a soft whinny reached his ears, and, to his great surprise, a pony came from behind the Mosque and slowly made its way to Peko.

"Hello, old fellow," murmured Peko, as he gently rubbed the pony's forehead. "I expect you are just as alone in the world as I am, so you'd better come along with me. We'll be company for one another. Anyway, you can carry my knapsack for a time," and he strapped it on the pony.

"What's your name?" The animal seemed to shake its head. "You don't know. Then I'll give you one. Your name will be Gavrilo, after our hero, Gavrilo Princip. Let's go."

Together the two travelers went in search of the Partisans. Climbing, always climbing, sometimes in single file, because of the narrow, precipitous path, they eventually came to a pine forest, where a path led to a narrow valley.

"Let's try this," murmured Peko to Gavrilo. "It should lead us somewhere."

It did indeed lead somewhere as Peko discovered, when a strident voice commanded him to halt.

"Who are you?" came the first question.

"I'm Peko."

His interrogator still remained hidden.

"Don't move, because my gun is aimed at you. What do you want?"

"I've come to join the Partisans."

"Give me the password."

"I don't know the password," answered Peko. "If Father Ribar is with you, then I have a message for him."

"Who sent you?"

"My own priest, Father Jovanovic."

"Where are you from?"

"My home was in the foothills of these mountains."

"Did you bring the pony from there?"

"No, Gavrilo . . ."

"Is that his name?" asked the sentry.

"Yes, I found him in the Moslem village below, which has been completely destroyed. He was alone, like me, so I took him along. I named him Gavrilo . . ."

"Don't tell me why," came the supercilious comment, "especially as I come from Sarajevo, where our hero, Gavrilo Princip, assassinated the Archduke Ferdinand. Put your hands up and come forward."

As Peko came forward, hands above his head, holding his fishing rod, Gavrilo following him, the sentry became visible. Then another voice broke the silence, this time a girl's voice.

"Who are you talking to Ivo? Are you talking to yourself?"

"No, Olga, there's a young lad here asking for Father Ribar."

"Did he give you the password?"

"No, comrade Olga."

"Then why didn't you shoot him? Anybody can ask for Father Ribar, especially as many of his parish came with him. This person may be a stool pigeon, or someone sent to spy out the land."

"I'm not," protested Peko. "I've marched miles to join the Partisans, I must join them. I am now all alone in the world."

"Keep your hands up, while I look at you."

Olga stepped out of the shadows.

Fifteen years old, she wore a tattered German tunic over a once-white blouse, grimy breeches tucked into high boots, which appeared to be held together by string, and her black hair was crowned by a forage cap, decorated with a five-pointed star. Around her waist was a girdle, from which hung half a dozen hand grenades. Her grimness detracted from her good looks, but there was something vital about her. She was obviously someone to be depended on in an emergency.

She ran experienced hands over Peko to see if he carried a weapon.

"What have you got in that knapsack?"

"They are the groceries I bought this morning for my family."

"Then why . . . ?"

"They were all shot dead by the Nazis."

Olga decided to ask no more questions. Peko seemed so transparently honest, she would take a chance.

"Follow me, and bring your pony with you."

In a clearing of the forest, around a low fire, six men were seated, cleaning their rifles. They took great pride in having clean weapons. Weapons meant everything to them, especially as nearly every one of them was taken from the enemy at the cost of life and limb. Often through a hail of fire, weapons would be rescued from dead comrades.

A tall, gaunt, ascetic-looking man was standing by, stirring the contents of a large iron pot which hung over the fire. Around his waist was a girdle, like Olga's, from which hung an assortment of hand grenades.

He was Father Ribar.

The rest of the Partisans were sleeping on their beds of pine needles, under the tall majestic trees.

Olga introduced Peko to Father Ribar.

"We found him outside. He says he has a message for you."

It was evident to the priest that Peko was pretty well exhausted.

"Take that load from off your pony's back, my son, and come and sit down beside me."

Peko unstrapped his knapsack and handed it to Olga.

"We will keep it for you," said Olga.

"No, please," said Peko, "share it with everybody."

"Now, Peko, my son, speak."

"Father Jovanovic sent me to you," and in a few sentences he described the massacre of his family.

"You couldn't have a better recommendation. You must be hungry." He handed Peko a hunk of black bread and a tin mug of hot potato soup.

The father was delighted when Peko crossed himself before he ate.

"You're a good boy, Peko. Don't let these atheists around here corrupt you," he added with a pleasant chuckle.

When Peko had eaten, he sank wearily to the ground.

"We'll look after the pony," said Father Ribar. "You close your eyes."

In a moment, he was fast asleep. Olga covered him with a blanket.

It was not the sun, not the songbirds, nor the usual busy clatter of the Partisans preparing for the day that awakened Peko. It was Olga's boot, gently prodding him.

"Awake, there's a lot to do."

Peko sprang to his feet. He was ashamed to have overslept.

"Go and wash yourself," ordered Olga, "or have a bath, which-ever you please"—she pointed to a crystal-clear mountain stream —"but be quick about it."

Peko decided to wash, and then reported immediately to Olga.

"I'll take you to our leader."

In a hut made of branches, with a piece of canvas for a roof, sat Rudi, the company commander, poring over a map. He was a young lieutenant of the former Yugoslav Army, and although a hard and ruthless disciplinarian, his detachment had a deep affection for him.

"This is Peko," said Olga, introducing the lad.

"Father Ribar has spoken to me about you," said the commander. "So you want to join our company of Partisans?"

"Yes, sir."

"Good. We'll have you"—and Rudi smiled. "There are one or two things for you to remember. Foremost, discipline and obedience. Then, a Partisan is an honest man. No looting and no stealing. His word is his bond, except, of course, to the enemy. Olga, take charge of Peko, and starting training him at once."

Olga led the boy away, but decided to give him breakfast before "breaking him in," as she put it. A tin mug of *ersatz* coffee—taken from the groceries Peko had brought into camp—and two pieces of black bread were the ration.

"Have you ever fired a rifle?" asked Olga, as she lovingly handled her own submachine gun.

"Yes, Comrade Olga."

"You can drop the 'comrade,' Peko."

"Yes, Olga."

"Who taught you?"

"My father."

"Are you a good shot?"

"People say that I am."

"How good are you?"

"I can bring a bird down out of the sky."

Olga looked searchingly at Peko. Was he spinning a yarn?

"Well, we can't afford to waste even a single bullet to prove your boast," said Olga, "but you'll soon have a chance to show what kind of marksman you are. And I suppose you're just as good at bomb and grenade throwing?"

"No, Olga, I have never thrown one."

"Good, then there's something I can teach you."

By the second day, Olga was quite proud of her pupil, and gave him a little grudging praise.

"Always remember," she impressed upon Peko, "that we don't want any heroics. The grenade is to kill the enemy, and not to blow yourself to pieces. Is that understood?"

"Yes, Olga."

"Then I will draw four for you from the quartermaster. Hang them from your belt, like we all do."

Peko had become a full Partisan.

At dusk that evening all the Partisans attended a conference presided over by the commander.

"For six days," he said, "we have been pinned down here by the enemy. Some of you say attack; others are more prudent. We are not cowards. We have proved that. But, if we attack the unknown, who can tell what the result will be? We cannot afford to lose men. We may even be wiped out."

"On the other hand, Rudi," interrupted Boris, a stocky little Bosnian, "there's no point in sitting here until the enemy is strong enough to surround and kill us. We must fight."

"There is much sense in what you say, Boris," continued the commander. "If we liberate the village the enemy is holding, we can set up direct communication with other groups of ours. But it's no good making an attack if we don't know their strength. It would be invaluable to us to know what the strength of the enemy is. We need a scout or two to spy out the land."

Like a shot came Peko's offer.

"I will go, sir."

Every head turned to the young lad.

"This is my own country. I was brought up here. I know every footpath, and all the peasants and farmers know me."

It was a slight exaggeration, but in his enthusiasm to show what he could do, Peko felt justified in overstating his case.

"And I will go with him," came from Olga. "I speak German,

and I have some ideas that I would like to talk over with you, Rudi."

At dawn the following day, seen off by Rudi and Father Ribar, Olga and Peko set out on their mission. The transformation in the girl was miraculous. The uniform and all the paraphernalia of a Partisan had been discarded. She wore a colored peasant blouse, a skirt, normal shoes, and a brightly colored scarf over her head. She was a typical Bosnian schoolgirl.

Peko had his knapsack on his back and was armed with his fishing rod.

"You are in charge, Olga," said Rudi. "Be prudent. Nazi sentries will be on the alert, and may fire first and ask questions later."

"God bless you both," said the priest, "and bring you safely back. We will be waiting for you, and so will Gavrilo. I will look after your pony, Peko."

The boy led the way down the mountainside. The path was narrow and it was like looping-the-loop. Without saying anything, Olga could not help admiring Peko's agility. It was an effort on her part to keep up with him.

She was glad when, after an hour, Peko called a halt by a mountain stream, and from his knapsack he produced some black bread and some strips of venison.

Then, preparing his fishing rod, he cast the line into the stream.

But Olga noticed that tears were running down Peko's cheeks. She could guess the reason.

"Don't cry for the dead, Peko. It won't help them. It's for the living we must cry. They need our tears and our help."

"But you don't understand, Olga. Sitting here and fishing, reminds me of my father. All my family . . ."

"Don't tell me that I don't understand," interrupted Olga. "You think that I'm hard. I have seen too much of death. I have no tears left in me. I was in Belgrade, where we lived, on Palm Sunday, 1941. Never in history was there anything so horrible as when the Nazis rained death and destruction on us from the skies. I was in High School—I have two more years to go—and when I finally went home three weeks later, my father was hanging from a lamppost, with a signboard 'Spring flowers of Belgrade,' and my mother had been raped before being murdered. Our home was razed to the ground. Have you ever seen a church desecrated and burned down, with the whole congregation inside, just because they were Serbs? And you tell me, Peko, that I don't understand."

A fish was tugging at the line. Peko hauled it in. It was a good-sized trout. He called it a day when he had collected three trout and a fine salmon.

"These are going to be first-class bait," said Olga as they resumed their walk. They came to a forest, but before they entered it, Olga suggested that they both roll in the leaves and the dust.

"Remember, we have been traveling for days. We have come from Jezero."

There was no need for them to hide from any patrol. They were brother and sister making their way to Sarajevo. The Partisans had burned their house, and had threatened to kill the two children on their next visit to the town. For safety, the parents were sending the children to an aunt and uncle in Sarajevo, where there were plenty of good opportunities with the Army of Occupation.

They were striding along in a carefree manner, Olga holding the four fish, when a German command to halt froze them in their tracks.

"Put your hands above your heads and advance slowly," came the order.

Olga whispered a translation to Peko, and the two of them obeyed. They reached a German sentry whose machine gun was pointed at them.

"Who are you and what are you doing here?"

Olga began her story.

"You speak German," interrupted the sentry.

"I learned it at High School. My brother has not yet reached the class in which German is taught."

"It will now be taught in all classes," said the sentry.

"Of course, sir," agreed Olga.

"Where are you from and where are you going?"

Olga launched into a breathless narrative, explaining why they were on the road, and ending by offering a fish to the sentry.

"Where did you get them from?" he asked.

"My brother caught them in the stream about two kilometers from here, with this rod"—and she pointed to it.

"When we have driven those cursed Partisans out of their rat holes, I will do some fishing. I live near the Rhine and we used to catch Rhine salmon. My son, who is ten, often went fishing with me," and from a wallet he promptly produced snapshots of himself with his wife, son, and two daughters.

"How lovely they are!" said Olga, and prompted Peko to say the same, even if it was in Yugoslav.

"But I am forbidden to take a fish from you," said the soldier. "You must first offer them to the captain. Anyway, I must take you to him."

He gave a low whistle, and from the forest came another sentry to whom he explained what he was going to do. Telling Peko and Olga to march straight ahead, he followed behind until they came to a clearing in the forest. Around a caravan were grouped tents and army trucks, and here, too, men were cleaning their rifles and machine guns. From a small field kitchen came the appetizing scent of food.

The German soldier first approached a sergeant to explain why he wanted to see the captain. The sergeant agreed that it was necessary, and the two of them and Olga and Peko made their way to the caravan, where the captain was reading a book, and where the sergeant asked permission to speak.

This being granted, the soldier then retold Olga's story, but the captain was a little more inquisitive.

"You speak German?"

"I do, sir," answered Olga. "My brother has not yet reached a high enough class."

"Where are you from?"

"From Jezero, a small place about six miles from Jajce. It was very beautiful there until the Partisans destroyed most of it."

"How long have you been walking?"

"For three days. At night we sleep in the woods or the forest. Sometimes a kind farmer gives us a ride for a kilometer or two."

"What about food?"

"We started out with some bread and venison, and since then we live off the land. We know what roots are good and what fruit or berries to eat. Besides we have a few dinars"—and she showed a handful of small-value notes—"with which we can buy something, if we're lucky. But generally, sir, we don't need to, like with these fish, which my brother caught. We make a little fire and grill them, but not a big salmon like this. Please, sir, may I offer it to you as a gift?"

The captain laughed.

"My goodness, you can rattle on, can't you? Yes, I'll accept the salmon. It's a long time since I ate some. When did you catch it?"

"Only about an hour ago," said Olga, "in the mountain stream, about two kilometers from here. You ought to fish there, sir."

"We will when we've finished those swine in the mountains. Did you see any Partisans on your way here?"

"We saw some yesterday," said Olga, "but we hid from them until they had passed."

"Where was it?"

Olga gave a reference miles away from her own people.

"No, we're not after them. We're after a lot hiding about three or four kilometers from here."

"I hope you'll pay them back for what the Partisans did to us."

"We will, don't worry."

"Oh, look!" exclaimed Olga excitedly. "Look, a tank!"

There, beneath a tall oak, stood a tank, being cleaned and polished by Nazi soldiers.

"I've never seen one before," said Olga. "I've seen pictures of tanks but never a real one, never a real German tank. Do you lead your men in that, sir?"

"Sometimes," answered the proud captain, "and sometimes the sergeant here is in it, or even both of us."

"Oh, wonderful!" cooed Olga.

"Would you like to go inside the tank?" asked the captain.

"Oh, sir, it would be the wish of my life granted, to have been inside a German tank."

The captain led the way. Olga explained to Peko what was happening. The men by the tank stood to attention, while the officer explained that the sergeant would take Olga and Peko inside the tank to show them the mechanism. Then he left to return to his caravan.

The two children were delighted with their adventure, and as a reward for his kindness, they asked the sergeant to accept a trout, which he gladly did.

"With such a wonderful tank," said Olga, "you will crush those tin soldiers in the mountains."

"We could do that easily enough," boasted the sergeant, "but between you and me, we've got some artillery on the way, and the guns will blast them out before we crush every one of them."

"Oh, what a pity we won't be here then," exclaimed Olga.

"It won't be for a couple of days yet, but it's going to be real fireworks."

"We hope to be in Sarajevo by then, but I expect we will hear about your victory there," flattered Olga, "especially if you, Sergeant, are in the tank."

"Would you like to eat with me before you go?" asked the sergeant.

"That's kind of you," answered Olga. "We would then be sure of one good meal today."

She translated this to Peko, whose grin and shining eyes were sufficient praise for Olga's handling of the situation.

At a proper table, on good tin plates, a three-course meal was served to the sergeant and his guests. They began with a thick yellow pea soup, followed by hamburger steaks, potatoes and cabbage, and finished with stewed fruit and a cup of real coffee.

While they were eating, Olga and Peko noticed that they had two wireless transmitters. One of them was in operation.

"Do you really get messages on that radio?" asked Olga naïvely.

"Oh, yes," answered the sergeant, "and we can send messages to other companies and to our headquarters."

"Oh, how wonderful! And now we must go on our way, or we will never reach our goal. We won't interrupt the captain, but please thank him for his kindness, and thank you, sir, for all your great kindness, and for giving us such an interesting time. Heil Hitler! Come, Peko."

"I had better take you past our sentries," volunteered the sergeant, "or you may run into trouble."

Acting on Peko's suggestion, he and Olga took a somewhat circuitous route so that they could see how well the rear of the German camp was protected, and what was the best road running past it.

Still clinging to the two trout, which they intended giving Father Ribar for his Friday meal, they returned to their base with all possible speed. They reported to their commander, and Peko drew a plan of the German camp, while Olga filled in the details, with Peko interrupting to say how wonderful Olga had been.

"Never mind the compliments," said Rudi, "save those for when we've got rid of the enemy."

A conference of section leaders was called, and it was decided that the Partisans dare not wait, but must attack. Zero hour was to be dawn the next morning. A night attack was impossible, because of the terrain. A plan of campaign was drawn up.

"May I please ask a favor?" requested Olga.

"Ask, and we'll see," answered Rudi.

"May Peko and I deal with the tank if they use it? We've got an idea."

"Tell me about it later," said Rudi.

At the end of the conference, Olga and Peko outlined their own particular campaign, depending, as Olga said, "on Peko's proving that his boast of being a good shot is not a vain one."

Dawn broke fine, and every Partisan moved quickly to the allotted position. Ten of them took the road that led to the rear of the German camp. Peko made himself comfortable and invisible behind a rock, from which he commanded the road, the only road along which the tank could move and maneuver. Olga was invisible.

The Partisans moved forward under cover, planning to be within firing range of the enemy before they were discovered. Their luck held. A shower of grenades rained on the rear of the camp before the first sentry saw the advance party of the Partisans and gave the alarm.

Well disciplined, the Germans were soon defending their rear, and preparing to attack the advancing Partisans. Their chief weapon was the tank, in which the captain led his men. It came trundling along the one road, as predicted by Olga.

Suddenly it stopped. In front of it had been built a high fence of branches which seemed impassable, but which could easily be brushed aside and crushed by the tank. However, Olga had gambled correctly on human curiosity. The captain poked his head out of the turret to view the obstacle, and Peko proved that he was not an idle boaster. A bullet hit the captain squarely between the eyes. He slumped across the front of the tank and, as his body was pulled down, Olga hidden in the thick vegetation beside the road, sprang forward, murmuring "Good for you, Peko," and dropped the grenade into the turret.

A few seconds of pandemonium inside the tank followed, during which the sergeant tried to get out, and suffered a similar fate to his captain. The explosion occurred, and Olga dropped another grenade into the tank. After the second explosion, all was silent.

The loss of their captain and sergeant, and the breakdown of their tank, broke the morale of the Germans, and they decided on a speedy retreat. Their camp was overrun by the Partisans, and much booty was collected, including a greatly prized wireless transmitter and receiver. Every gun, all the ammunition, and the uniforms of every dead German soldier—and there were forty-six of them—were collected. The arms and ammunition of the seven dead Partisans were also brought in. The Germans were buried in a mass grave. The Partisans were given a Christian burial by Father Ribar.

Once again the little village changed hands, and there could be no doubt where the sympathies of the inhabitants lay. For two weeks the Partisans lived in comparative luxury. Then came the news, brought by a farmer from a village ten miles away, that the Germans had regrouped, that they had a sizable force of artillery and that they had cleared a space large enough for an airplane to land. Their force numbered about three hundred.

A hurried conference was called, and it was agreed with Rudi that "discretion is the better part of valor," and to save the little village from being completely wiped out and the inhabitants from being massacred, the Partisans would move back into their mountain camp.

But they could chalk up two notable achievements. Thirty-two villagers joined the Partisans, and, best of all, the village doctor, a young woman named Zdenka, joined them. Headquarters allotted them a radio operator, which gave the group a distinction and a status they had long wished to have.

It was winter, 1942–43. Although their new hideout in the mountains was almost impregnable—except from the air, where the German planes were constantly searching—the Partisans had to fight a grim, and often losing, battle against the weather.

The snow was deep, the cold intense. The breath froze in the cold. It was often fifty degrees below zero, and when a blizzard came, the icy particles stung like red-hot needles, and sentries had to indulge in constant dancing movements to prevent their boots from freezing to the ground.

The sentry, who inhabited the tank which had been incorporated as a defense strong point, considered himself lucky to have a little shelter. Someone had named the tank *Olga* and had painted the name on it.

A message had come through early one morning from the nearest Partisan detachment that there was to be an airdrop in their camp at midnight, if conditions were favorable. Would Rudi send a party to collect their allotment? Six Partisans were immediately chosen. Olga and Peko were two of them, and the pony, Gavrilo, was to go with them to carry the main burden.

The six of them carried knapsacks, and the four men had two sizable handcarts to push along.

"If anything hinders the drop tonight," ordered Rudi, "then stay on until it does occur. If it happens tonight, make sure that you get our allotment, stay overnight, and start out early in the morning."

"And make sure that you get the medical supplies I ordered," added Dr. Zdenka.

With a happy neigh from Gavrilo, and well wrapped up, the party set off in good spirits. The road was mostly downhill, and, with great care and by helping one another, they marched the five miles to their destination in six hours.

They received a warm welcome, with a special meal for Gavrilo. After a rest, they helped prepare the ground for the drop. A large clearance was made in case the pilot decided to land, as one or two of them had done. Fifteen minutes before midnight, a faint hum of engines was heard in the clear still night. *"Avioni"*—planes —murmured a Partisan as he lit the signal fires. "Pray God they are ours," for it was not unknown for the enemy to arrive on such an occasion and drop its load of bombs.

They were "our planes," one British and one American. From the British plane two men fell out, their parachutes opened, and they landed on the prepared ground. They were members of the British Mission, sent as liaison officers with the Partisans.

From both planes came a shower of parachutes with their loads. The pilots maneuvered their planes splendidly. Few parachutes fell far afield, and these were quickly brought in by willing hands. Their mission accomplished, the planes flew off, and the fires were quickly put out.

At first light, Olga and Peko, and the four men, were ready to start on the return journey. Each of them had a full knapsack, the handcarts were stacked with all they could hold, and Gavrilo had all the load it was possible for the pony to bear.

Climbing, all the time climbing, it was tough going, and after two hours they were happy to find a natural cave in the mountainside, in which they could rest and enjoy a brief meal of bread and strips of venison. Half an hour was all they allowed themselves, and once more knapsacks on their backs, they resumed their climb, often along precipitous pathways.

It was fortunate for them that the winter sun shone from a cloudless sky and that there was no wind. Yet, because it was a fine, clear day, misfortune befell them. They heard the hum of a plane engine when they were on a narrow plateau which offered them no cover. It could be a friendly plane, but the Partisans had been trained to be cautious. They tried to reach the shelter of some rocks ahead, but the slippery ground made speedy progress impossible.

The plane spotted them before they could find any shelter. It was a German fighter. It flew low and spattered them with bullets from its stuttering machine guns. Suddenly Olga spun round and fell on her face. Peko moved to her as quickly as he could, leaving Gavrilo to look after himself. By the time he reached her, the blood was already staining the snow red.

Vlatko, the strongest of the group, helped Peko to carry Olga to comparative safety behind some rocks, as the plane made a return flight to fire again. They unstrapped her knapsack and made a pillow of it, and tried to locate the wound. Peko tore off his German greatcoat and laid it on the snow, then ripped off his shirt and made bandages of it to staunch the blood which appeared to flow from a wound in the chest, above her left breast.

Olga clenched her teeth and didn't murmur.

"It will be all right," whispered Peko, "we'll soon have you in camp."

A faint smile crossed Olga's bloodless face.

"Let's unload Gavrilo," suggested Peko, "and put Olga on the pony."

"No," answered Vlatko. "We must bring the stores in. We'll manage to put Olga's knapsack on the pony, and we'll take turns in carrying her in your greatcoat. Meanwhile, Peko, put my tunic on. It will make an overcoat for you or, in this weather we'll have two casualties. We must go on. To sit down is to die."

It was a nightmare of a march to all of them, and the sun was setting as they straggled into camp, weary and footsore.

Olga was immediately taken into a shed that the Partisans had built to serve as a hospital. Peko refused to rest. He went with her, and Doctor Zdenka decided on an immediate operation, without anesthetic. By the light of a hurricane lamp, which Peko held, the doctor searched and probed for the bullet.

"Stop shaking the lamp, or I will ask for somebody else," muttered Zdenka to the trembling boy.

"Yes, sir," he answered.

"And don't call me sir."

"No, sir," came from the distraught Peko.

The bullet was found and extracted, the wound bandaged, and a sleeping pill sent Olga into a deep, dreamless sleep. Peko again refused to turn in for the night. Father Ribar tried to persuade him to do so, but was kindly and sympathetic in his understanding of the boy's loyalty and faithfulness. Peko sat the night through at Olga's bedside, every now and again dropping off to sleep. When morning came, Father Ribar offered to relieve Peko, but the boy wouldn't budge.

"See," whispered the priest, "Olga's awake."

The girl opened her eyes, looked at the lad, said "Hello, Peko," smiled, and closed her eyes again. Then the floodgates opened. Peko broke down and sobbed like a boy of fourteen should. Father Ribar gently led him away.

During Olga's convalescence the priest arranged for Peko to act as "hospital orderly," especially attached for duty to Olga. The highlight of the day for the two children was the visit of Father Ribar, who brought them the good news of the Allied successes.

"My children, we are winning. Our war of National Liberation is succeeding. We are no longer an accursed nation of bits and pieces. We are no longer Serbs, Macedonians, Montenegrins, Bosnians, Herzegovinians, Croats, Slovenes. We are Yugoslavs, with no hatred for each other and no distinction about race. Rejoice, my children, you are going to live in a wonderful world, for which you have truly fought."

It was 1943, and the road to victory was rough and costly. The Partisan group had now become part of a 20,000-strong Partisan army which, in one offensive by 160,000 German soldiers—specially trained in Alpine warfare, with artillery and aircraft—suffered severe losses, with 4,500 wounded. On one occasion, boys and girls brought in on their backs hundreds of wounded from the firing line to the hospital, miles away.

Olga and Peko did more than their normal share. They destroyed enemy communications, ambushed convoys, raided stores for food, which was badly needed, since the Partisans often had to fall back on unproductive mountain regions already made desolate by the enemy. For lack of fodder, the horses had to be eaten. It was only by a miracle, and sheer guile on the part of Olga and Peko that Gavrilo escaped slaughter.

Supply drops from the air by the British and Americans were lifesavers for the Partisans.

In 1944 there was another hard winter, but with the spring came the days when the enemy was on the retreat. Village after village, town after town, was being liberated by the Partisans. Everywhere they were welcomed, too often by refugees straggling along the road, with rags tied around their feet or barefoot, carrying children who were too weak and too hungry to cry.

One day Olga and Peko were summoned by Rudi and informed that they had been chosen as representatives of their group to attend a Congress of Youth to be held in Drvar, a town about a hundred miles away. Rudi mapped out a route for them, and told them they would have to manage as best they could. They persuaded Rudi to allow them to take Gavrilo with them, and, with Father Ribar's blessing, they set out on what became an eventful and hazardous journey, often on foot, and often through enemy-occupied areas.

But they reached the small ruined Bosnian town, where the Germans had taken a terrible revenge against the civilians because it was in this town that the Germans had once just failed to capture Tito.

It was May Day, and the Congress was to begin the next day, and to last for four days. Olga and Peko were tremendously excited as they filed into the hall with about eight hundred delegates, having found good stabling for Gavrilo. Great enthusiastic cheers greeted "Churchill's son," Major Randolph Churchill, when he spoke to them in Serbo-Croatian, and praised their many achievements.

The Congress ended as Olga and Peko, and the many hundreds like them, made this promise, "We swear by our honor, by the endeavor and sacrifice of our people and our youth, that we shall spare neither our lives nor our strength in the struggle for freedom, for conscience, for the honor and the future of every young man and woman of Yugoslavia."

SS5: PAGES FROM JAN'S DIARY

MAY 9, 1940

This is the first diary I have ever had, and I am itching to write in it. It also has a lock and key.

Tomorrow is my birthday, and it is a present from my parents. It was given to me yesterday, because my father, who is a doctor, was called up to join the army. But I am sure that this mobilization is another false alarm, because Hitler has promised faithfully not to invade Holland. So we expect Father to get leave to spend my birthday as we planned it.

I will be fourteen tomorrow, and my four best school friends, Piet and Charlotte, the "carrot twins," because of their fiery hair, and Hendrik and Jos are joining Father, Mother, and me.

We live in a suburb of Amsterdam. We will begin my birthday celebration with a tour of the city by boat, gliding through the famous *grachten* [canals]. (This is really to please Charlotte.)

Then we will go to the Rijksmuseum, which is our National Gallery. It makes me proud to be Dutch, when I look at the paintings by Frans Hals, Jan Steen, Vermeer, and especially Rembrandt. I am going to buy a copy of his best-known work *The Night Watch*.

Then we will have lunch at Zandvoort aan Zee. I like this seaside resort.

In the evening we are going to Haarlem, because there is to be an organ recital in Saint Bavo Church. We are all fond of music, and I love this organ, which is one of the most famous in the world. It has three keyboards, sixty-eight registers, and five thousand pipes. It was built in 1738, and my father tells me that Mozart and Handel played on it. It must have been wonderful to hear the playing of such famous musicians, and I get a tremendous feeling of peace and happiness whenever I hear it.

The weatherman says it is going to be fine tomorrow. Hurrah!

May 10

Mother awoke me this morning. One look at her serious face, and I knew that something was wrong. She kissed me and said, "Happy Birthday," but it was so unlike my mother, who is a very jolly person. This morning it was all very sad.

I could now hear distant thuds.

"What is it?" I asked.

"The Germans have invaded Holland. I pray for Father, and for our poor country."

I washed and dressed very quickly, and went down into the street. Everybody had a different story to tell. Schiphol airport was on fire, but some soldiers—they were fifth columnists in Dutch uniforms I learned later—said that we were doing well and beating back the Germans.

May 11, 12, 13

These have been chaotic days. The Queen has moved from her house *Huis ten Bosch* into the palace in the center of The Hague.

No news about Father. We are worried.

May 14

We have been told that the Queen has decided to leave the country. A British destroyer took her to England yesterday, where she has been joined by her Cabinet.

For a moment it looked like desertion, but, as my mother explained to me, the struggle against Hitler will be carried on from there, and from here, I hope.

Still no news about Father.

MAY 15

I can't believe it, but it is true. The Nazis have destroyed Rotterdam by air bombardment. It must be the greatest crime ever committed by one nation against another. They threaten to do the same to other towns unless we surrender.

We have surrendered. But I'm glad the oil tanks near the Noordzee canal have been set on fire. I would have liked to have done that!

Everybody is rushing to Ymuiden to try and board a boat for England.

Some of us must stay behind to fight.

Still no news of Father. We are so worried.

MAY 16

The German Army came into Amsterdam yesterday. Only the fifth column, who stabbed us in the back, welcomed them. Most of us stayed at home in silence. I hear that many people, especially Jews or refugees from Germany, have committed suicide rather than live under the Nazis.

And the Germans keep repeating on the radio that they have come as friends. Tell that to the people of Rotterdam!

Some reservists have returned home. But no sign of Father.

JUNE 4

The Nazis are trying all their tricks to win over the schoolchildren. They have given us sweets which most of us have put down the drain, and they have allowed the top class to matriculate without passing the exams.

Our teacher says, "Be brave. Hold your heads up."

Poor Mother. I wish I could do something to find out about Father.

JUNE 9

I have decided that we must do all we can to make life unpleasant for the Nazis. We have formed a Secret Society—me, Piet, Jos, and Hendrik. But Charlotte, Piet's twin sister, has found out about us, and insists on joining. I told her that this isn't a job for girls. "Don't be so superior," she said.

I explained that we're not being superior. There may be danger, and the Nazis don't care whom they torture. Charlotte then threatened that if we don't take her in with us, she would work on her own. Besides, she said, a girl can do things that a boy can't.

So now we are the Secret Society Five—the SS5, we call ourselves for fun.

Good news we hope. Mother went, as usual, to Church this morning. As she knelt to pray, a young woman knelt beside her. "Don't look at me, Mrs. Jonkheer," she whispered, "and don't show any surprise. Keep on praying. Don't worry about your husband. He is safe in London. He sends his love to you and Jan." Then she rose and vanished.

Please God it's true.

JUNE 15

A German officer came into our classroom this morning. We have a large picture of our Queen Wilhelmina in a prominent place. He saw this, and in deadly silence he ripped out the picture, tore it up, and screamed at us.

"You ungrateful beasts to behave so. We are giving you a wonderful life and a wonderful education. You are now part of the glorious Third Reich, which our Führer has promised will last a thousand years. We are kind to you, but we can also punish. Remember that. Heil Hitler!"

And out he stormed.

JUNE 16

In classroom this morning, right across the empty frame, in which had been the Queen's picture, were large words, TEMPORARILY ABSENT.

First score to Charlotte.

JUNE 17

Charlotte has discovered in which hotel the officer who insulted our Queen is staying. She kept track of his car. Tonight, in the darkness, she has decorated the back with a large W in orange paint, and emptied the rest of the bucket on the back seat of the car.

We have decided that we must have a safe and secret place to meet.

Jos, who is our little imp, said, "Leave it to me."

JUNE 19

True to his word, Jos, who lives farther out of the town than we do, has found us a wonderful hideout. It is an old dilapidated barn on Farmer Smit's farm. Not only has the farmer—we know he is 100 percent loyal Dutch—given us permission to use it, but he has shown Jos a hidden trapdoor that leads to an underground cellar.

JUNE 21

Report of the first meeting in our hideout.

The main item to discuss was Prince Bernhard's birthday on the twenty-ninth of June, eight days away. The Nazis have forbidden any national or orange-colored flags. What are we going to do? Charlotte proposed that we tell everybody to wear a white carnation. It is the Prince's favorite flower. We could pass the word on, like a chain letter, to all the big cities and especially the Universities. But, said Jos, the Nazis and the fifth columnists will only tear them out of our buttonholes. "Not if you follow my plan," said Hendrik. (It is not for nothing we call Hendrik "the Professor.") He suggested that we beg, borrow, or steal old and new razor blades from our fathers, brothers and uncles. Break them into small pieces and hide them in the flowers.

We agreed to this unanimously, and pledged ourselves to spread this plan far and wide through all our friends.

JUNE 26

Our idea has caught on like a grand chain letter. We're going to have fun.

JUNE 29

Prince Bernhard's birthday.

Crowds are everywhere wearing white carnations. We exchange merry greetings, as though it's our own birthdays. The Nazis are furious. To our delight, they have issued an order, "Tear every carnation from buttonhole or dress." We did not resist as fingers bled, and the streets were spattered with the blood of the cursing and cursed Nazis. A notable victory for SS5.

JULY 5

At the next meeting of our SS5 we had a surprise and a shock. In a corner of the cellar, on a rickety table, stood an ancient radio. Pinned to it was a note, "For the attention of the Professor."

Was it a trick? Somebody knows Hendrik's nickname and our hideout.

"Wait," said Jos. "Don't touch it until I come back."

Within a few minutes we learned that it was a gift from Farmer Smit. Hendrik had no difficulty in fixing it.

We can now listen comfortably to the BBC from London.

We decided to fix a schedule to listen in. We can't all be away from home every night, or from our usual places. Otherwise we will excite suspicion, apart from giving our families anxious moments. Piet warned us to be very careful, as there are traitors everywhere. We've even one in our class.

The traitor in our class is Klaus, nicknamed "The Rat." He belongs to the Nazi Youth Organization, and we make life hell for him, especially when he wears a uniform.

No further news about Father. We are anxious.

JULY 28

Tonight we listened to our Queen speaking for the first time on Radio Orange. It was wonderful. She said it was a battle between God and our conscience on one side, and the forces of darkness on the other. Nothing will ever succeed in exterminating our love for liberty. Even though the enemy has occupied our native soil, we will carry on the war until a free and happy future dawns for us.

We all felt like cheering. Except Charlotte. I asked her what was wrong. She said that we are too easily satisfied. Laughing at the Nazis and having dreams isn't enough. It's kid's stuff. It may hurt their vanity, but what real damage do we do to their war effort?

Piet agreed with Charlotte. They had talked about this at home. They say that we've got to hit them where it hurts. I asked for any suggestions. Jos came up with one. Near his home is a farm of a NSB farmer. (NSB is the name we give to the Dutch Nazis—the

National-Socialistische Beweging.) The farmer is going to sell all his produce to the Nazis. He boasts about it. "Let's teach him a lesson," said Jos.

AUGUST 9

We had an interesting chemistry lesson today. Jos and Hendrik were taught about very inflammable substances.

"These chemicals must be handled with care," warned our chemistry teacher, but he appeared to forget to lock them away, as he always did at the end of a lesson. Nor did Jos and Hendrik rush out of the laboratory as the rest of the class did.

Still no news from Father, and Mother never met the lady in church again, although she goes there every morning. Mother is very sad.

AUGUST 10

No complaint from the chemistry teacher, even though half of his stock of inflammable materials is missing.

AUGUST 14

We have really hit them where it hurts, thanks to Jos and Hendrik.

This is the story Jos told us at a meeting of the SS5.

"The harvest of my farmer neighbor was in. The barns were bulging. It was two o'clock in the morning. I was lying on my bed, fully dressed, when I heard a special owl hoot. I knew that Hendrik was on his way to the farm.

"By a short cut, I reached the farm ahead of him. A low growl from the two Alsatian dogs greeted me, because they know me. I have often played with them, before the Nazis invaded us. I called softly to the dogs, and they came to me. They sniffed at me, and were happy to see me. I gave them a biscuit each and a piece of sausage saved from my ration. 'That's good boys. Now lie down quietly.' And they did.

"Suddenly they jumped up, all tense. I knew that Hendrik was near.

" 'Quiet, Muff—quiet, Nero,' I whispered to them, 'you must not make a noise. Just lie here next to me nice and quiet.' They did so.

"The next few minutes were like years. The dogs were restive. Then came another special owl hoot.

"I whispered to the dogs. 'Come with me, Muff. Come with me, Nero. There's good boys,' and led them to the kennels where I chained them.

"I had barely returned home by the short cut, when the barns burst into flame. I undressed quickly, got into bed, and when my father awoke me from what he thought was a deep sleep, the farm buildings were blazing fiercely.

" 'Come, Son,' said my father, 'Our neighbor's farm is on fire. Although we despise him, we must do what we can.' 'Of course, Father. I'll just put on my shoes, and my overcoat.'

"We reported to our neighbor, who was grateful for our help. I found two large cans of gasoline, marked 'For agricultural purposes,' in the garage. It was a pity to waste them. So I put the gasoline in buckets and poured it over one corner of the farm, where I was helping.

"By the time the fire department arrived the farm was completely destroyed. The captain of the firemen thanked me and my father for our public-spirited action. 'I wish there were more boys in Holland like you,' he said, and I murmured, 'Oh, there are.' We all congratulated Jos and Hendrik, and Charlotte added, 'At last some real action.' "

SEPTEMBER 5

We had a shock this morning when our friend, Farmer Smit, came into our classroom with the Nazi SS officer, who is now a frequent visitor at the school.

"I want volunteers," shrieked the Nazi, "to help with the harvest and with farmwork in the afternoons and at weekends."

Klaus the Rat immediately put up his hand up.

Farmer Smit looked at him, doubtfully, and then shook his head.

"No, it's patriotic of him, and I thank him, but he's too puny for the work I want done. It wouldn't be fair to him."

"Well, as there are no other volunteers," shouted the Nazi, "pick those you want."

Farmer Smit looked around the class, and pointed to Piet and to me. "They look strong enough to be likely workers—if they'll work."

"Stand up," screamed the officer. Piet and I stood up, but hung our heads, as though in shame. "Stand straight, you lazy dogs, and hold your heads up." Then he turned to Farmer Smit and said, "Make whatever use you want of them. And if there's any trouble, report it to me. I'll make an example of them."

"May I also have them all day, if necessary?" asked Smit timidly.

"Certainly. More useful than all this book muck."

"I will report this to the Director of Education," protested our teacher.

"Report till you're blue in the face," stormed the Nazi. "We need food, not book learning."

SEPTEMBER 6

Piet and I reported to the farm yesterday afternoon. We had a shrewd idea that Farmer Smit was up to something.

"I'm sorry that I couldn't warn you beforehand, but I thought it better to surprise you."

To our astonishment, in walked our schoolmaster.

"There's no time to waste," he said, and handed four small parcels to Farmer Smit. "It is all set as planned." Turning to us, he said, "Jan, Piet, you have not seen me, or heard me, even though I came to see that you had reported to Farmer Smit."

In a twinkling he was gone.

"Now that you are employed by me," said Farmer Smit, "you can accompany me when I deliver my produce. Tonight we have to deliver a truckload of beets some miles away." We reported at nine, and drove through the night fifteen miles to a storehouse, where the beets were unloaded, and where I saw Farmer Smit hand over to two men the four parcels our schoolmaster had given him. Behind the storehouse ran a lonely stretch of railway line. Piet was posted by it half a mile away, and I was posted half a mile the other way. We were to give a low bird call, if we saw anything or anybody suspicious.

Within five minutes the four parcels were tied to specially chosen points on the railway lines. At ten thirty, when we were six miles away on our return journey, we heard a terrific explosion.

SEPTEMBER 7

We have just heard that last night a German munitions train on its way to Belgium was derailed and destroyed.

SEPTEMBER 16

Piet and I were summoned from school to meet the German Food Commissioner on the farm. Farmer Smit was in a towering rage.

"Who is delivering the milk this week?" he shouted.

"He is," we each replied, pointing to the other.

"Do you know what has happened through your criminal carelessness?" he shrieked. "Two hundred and fifty liters of good milk have gone sour. Two hundred and fifty liters that should have gone to Germany! How can you be so stupid?" Then, with tears in his eyes, Farmer Smit turned to the Commissioner and said, "What can you expect when nine out of ten of the young people in our dear country revile our German friends? And when boys and girls at home are made to listen to the enemy radio from England? I make sure that these two boys don't." We hung our heads in shame as he shouted, "Let this be a warning to you."

"We couldn't come out at night," said Piet, "we dare not break the curfew." Farmer Smit then drew the Nazi into a corner and confided to him that although Piet and I were good workers, we made excuses that we could not look after the animals or deliver the milk because we were not allowed to be out at night, during prohibited hours.

"Clever monkeys," said the Commissioner, "we will provide them with passes. Come to my office in the morning, with their particulars. Heil Hitler!"

Ten minutes later, after a good reconnaissance, the three of us had a nice glass of fresh milk, and enjoyed a good laugh. At least 250 liters of good Dutch milk had not reached Germany. . . . But there is still no message from Father—we all five listen for it.

NOVEMBER 9

Our artists, Jos and Charlotte, are enjoying themselves these dark nights. They are specializing in painting false road signs.

Other young people do the same and many Nazi cars are fished out of the canals. We hope the eels have a good time.

Hendrik's favorite hobby is cutting telephone wires. He has become quite an expert and was especially pleased when one night he disrupted half the telephone system of Amsterdam.

Little Jos is sticking to arson.

Piet and I have passed our tests with Farmer Smit to drive a truck.

JANUARY 1, 1941

It's a very unhappy New Year for all of us. There has been one wonderful New Year's gift for my mother and me. We have received a message from my father from London. A piece of paper was pushed through the mailbox with a message that only my father could have sent, because he used the pet names for Mother and me, that only we know.

FEBRUARY 6

The Nazis are taking a terrible revenge for any acts of sabotage. No one knows whether he will be arrested by the Gestapo on a trumped-up charge, and tortured in prison, or a concentration camp.

Our SS5 must be more careful, but Charlotte is becoming restless because, being a girl, we give her less and less to do.

MARCH 20

We listened to the broadcast of Queen Wilhelmina from London. She spoke to us because the Nazis have executed thirty innocent people, following the destruction by fire of a flour mill, in which Jos had a hand.

She pleads with us to practice caution, and to refrain from being reckless.

MARCH 27

A grim silence, as usual, came over the class this morning, as the Nazi SS officer marched into the room with his "Heil Hitler." "I want clerical staff for our headquarters," he barked. "Particularly girls, who can type and who have a good knowledge of German, which I know you all have." Not a girl moved. "They will be well paid, and will receive double food rations."

After a slight pause, Charlotte rose in her seat. We all stared at her. This couldn't be true. The schoolmaster seemed to go white. This really couldn't be true.

But there Charlotte stood, indifferent to the muttered imprecations of her classmates with whom she had been so popular.

"I'm glad that there is one Dutch girl who knows where her duty lies," snapped the officer. "Come with me."

As Charlotte left the room, a dreadful low hiss followed her.

April 6

Charlotte is having a taste of purgatory. Her friends shun her. The neighbors don't speak to the family. Nobody greets her. She is insulted on every possible occasion. Even Piet avoids being with her in the open.

Only in her own home, and at an occasional meeting of the SS5 in our cellar, does she enjoy the love and admiration of her family and friends.

We know that Charlotte is gambling with her freedom, and maybe with her life. Nothing her sad and bewildered parents say can change her mind. She mentioned at our last meeting in a by-the-way remark that she hopes that SS5 will be very proud of her. More she did not say.

No further news about Father. Mother is worrying more and more.

April 21

We arranged for the SS5 to meet in full session tonight. It is a rare occasion now when we do so, but we want to listen because Hendrik said that there would be a special announcement from Radio Orange in London.

Four of us gathered round the radio. Charlotte was missing.

"So unlike her to be late," whispered Piet.

"Shall I go and scout for her?" asked Hendrik.

"No, decidedly no," I said. "If she is not here, there must be a reason for it—good or bad. Piet will know when he goes home."

The messages did come over the radio. They were:

"Eagles don't breed doves."

"By night all cats are gray."

"Better alone than in bad company."

We don't know what they mean, but we are sure they brought hope and comfort to some people.

APRIL 22

Charlotte's story, told to Piet, who related it to me this morning, was:

"The moment I left the Nazi headquarters this evening, I felt instinctively that all was not well. I casually looked up and down the street as I usually do before I cross the road. On one corner I saw a stranger lighting a cigar, but his eyes were more concentrated on me than on the cigar.

"Yet was he entirely a stranger? He looked very much like a Gestapo officer I had seen pass through my office once. I knew that they often checked up on employees—where they went, who they met, and so on.

"I was suspicious. I decided to make certain before attending our SS5 meeting. I walked slowly down the Herengracht where my shadower—I was sure he was following me—had little to hide him. The elm trees were hardly wide enough.

"From there I did some window shopping in the Leidsestraat, and I could see the reflection of this man, who was now casually looking into windows on the opposite side of the street. I then took him for a nice walk in Rokin, did some more window shopping, then stood before the Royal Palace, and finally went into Nieuwe Kerk (the New Church), which was open. I admit I was scared, and I really prayed very hard.

"I came out of the Church, drew a deep breath, congratulated myself on having shaken off my follower, when a voice said, 'What a wonderful church,' and there alongside me stood this man. He was all smiles as he raised his hat, but my heart was beating twenty to the dozen.

" 'Yes,' I replied, as calmly as I could, 'you must be a visitor to Amsterdam, not to know our Nieuwe Kerk, because all the Dutch sovereigns have been crowned here since William the First.'

" 'How interesting,' he said. 'I am a stranger. I am in the horticultural business, and I have come to buy bulbs.'

" 'You couldn't have come to a better place. You must go to Keukenhof where you will see millions of bulbs in bloom. It is a most beautiful sight. Nobody can equal Dutch bulbs.' Was I becoming too enthusiastic?

" 'Yes,' he said with a forced smile, 'only now you would call them German bulbs.'

" 'I don't know,' I answered, 'I keep out of politics. I leave that to the grown-ups.'

" 'Some young people are not as sensible as you. I suppose one can't blame them if they start fires, or do other acts of sabotage. It's only natural.'

" 'I wouldn't know. I'm glad to get home after my work, and my daily constitutional stroll. Good-bye, sir, I must go for my tram. Buy plenty of bulbs.'

"Off I went very smartly. Now I had really succeeded in shaking him off.

"Looking through the window of the tram, I saw the man on the pavement, obviously making notes about the route of the tram.

"I decided that I would definitely not attend the meeting of our SS5. On arriving home, for some inexplicable reason I carefully peeped through a corner of a front window. Slowly and thoughtfully the man passed by. I shivered."

APRIL 29

This morning we had a shock. Our schoolmaster was absent, and so was the headmaster. Piet and I waited for fifteen minutes, and then decided to act. We did not miss the gleam of triumph in the eyes of Klaus the Rat. Have we underestimated this informer? We had a quick talk with Hendrik and Jos, and then Piet and I slipped out of school and made for the farm.

We saw Farmer Smit, and within minutes I was on my way to Amsterdam to deliver messages to several people, and Piet was given his assignment.

Piet has an arrangement with Charlotte, that in extreme emergency he would sit at an outside table of the little café, facing the Nazi headquarters where Charlotte works. She would always look out through the window of her office at the beginning of her lunch break. Today she spotted the red head of her brother, Piet. She hurried down to join him in a cup of filthy *ersatz* coffee. Real coffee was unobtainable.

"I know what you've come about," she whispered casually, and even pretended to be gay. "They were arrested in the early morning as they left an underground printing press. They were carrying leaflets inciting people to sabotage. It looks pretty bad."

"Where are they?" asked Piet.

"In the Central Police Station. They are being transported to a German concentration camp at midnight."

"Get us two travel passes," said Piet, "one to Brussels and one to Antwerp. One for a commercial traveler in Delft china, and one for an engineer. Some rations cards, and two special identity cards. I'll meet you at our usual place at three o'clock."

Here is the story that Farmer Smit told Piet and me:

"At four o'clock in the afternoon, a high-ranking SS officer and five SS men, of which I was one, drove up to the Central Police Station.

" 'Keep the engine running,' said the officer to the driver as they entered the Police Station. The officer and the five of us entered the room of the Inspector in charge of the station. 'Bring all the men in here,' commanded the officer, 'something important has happened.'

"When all the police were in the room, he continued, 'We've just heard that a raid to release your prisoners is contemplated. Where are the Dutch dogs?'

" 'In the cellar, sir.'

" 'Good. Let's all go down there, and I will explain my plan.'

"When we were all in the cellar, the officer warned all of us that this might mean using our revolvers. 'I will examine all the guns to see that they are in good order. My own men first.'

"We presented our guns for inspection.

" 'Good. Now each of you examine the guns of the police.'

"Each policeman held out his gun. We took them, and kept them.

" 'Now,' said the SS officer, pointing his gun at the Inspector, 'we know how to treat enemies of the Reich. We know you were going to allow these prisoners to escape.'

" 'That's a lie,' stammered the Inspector. 'We are loyal to the

German Government. The prisoners are to be collected at midnight.'

" 'They won't live that long,' snarled the SS officer. 'Open the prison cell.'

"With trembling hands the Inspector did so.

" 'Come out here, you Dutch traitors,' shouted the officer.

"Blinking at the lights, the schoolmasters emerged.

" 'Take them upstairs, handcuff them, and if they attempt to escape, shoot to kill. And now'—he turned to the Inspector and his men—'into the cell, all of you, until you are removed to jail. The key.'

"Twenty minutes later the schoolmasters were dropped in a side street by the SS car, five minutes' walk from the station."

Piet and I were waiting there, each with a copy of a Nazi newspaper in which we had carefully placed the official papers Charlotte had stolen for us.

I also had a small suitcase with samples of Delft ware, which I gave to our schoolmaster.

We watched them enter the station, and followed at a safe distance.

The station was bristling with SS men, German soldiers on leave, police, secret police, high officers and Gestapo officials, and here and there a Dutch citizen. Our two travelers had no difficulties. Their papers were an open sesame. Even an offer to open the suitcase was politely refused.

We waited anxiously until the train pulled out of the station, and then heaved a great sigh of relief.

MAY 17

We had quite a thrill today. Farmer Smit and I were tuned in to Radio Orange. Over came the message for which we had been waiting, "Hey diddle-diddle, the cat and the fiddle, the cow jumped over the moon."

Our two schoolmasters had reached London safely.

And an additional postscript that gave my mother and me great joy—"The doctor sends his love to you both."

SEPTEMBER 21

Mother's birthday.

A wonderful present from Father. A special message through Radio Orange, full of love and good cheer. We are almost happy. Also Farmer Smit gave me six eggs for Mother.

OCTOBER 2

So far fortune has favored us, but we must exercise greater care. Hendrik has had a narrow squeak. He offered to repair a handpress on which patriotic news sheets were being printed. But for the quick presence of mind of Jos, who was on guard, six people would have been caught, and certainly shot. The Nazis are becoming desperate and ruthless in the fight against the Dutch patriots. Hostages are being seized on the slightest provocation.

We have to be extra careful.

OCTOBER 14

This has been a very exciting day, and for Piet and me it is only just beginning, even though I am writing this at six o'clock in the evening.

Charlotte has been wonderful. During her lunch hour at noon she phoned her mother from a café. A waiter, pretending not to listen, heard every word, but it was quite an innocent conversation.

"Hello, Mother dear, how are you? Is your migraine better?"

Charlotte's mother knew at once that something very important had happened. It was part of their own code.

"I am very worried about Uncle Smit. He looks terribly ill, and as if he might be taken from us at any moment. I know he loves his farm, but what good will it be to him if he dies, and he looks as if he will at any moment. Please insist, Mother, that he goes to the doctor straight away. Don't take No for an answer. That's all, Mother dear. Sorry to trouble you, but I am so worried. Bye-bye."

Charlotte had seen the list of hostages to be collected at midnight that night, and Farmer Smit's name was on it.

Within minutes of Charlotte's phone call, her mother made her way to the Smit farm, ostensibly to borrow a little tea and sugar.

Then she called in to the school to see Piet.

I must now go to meet Piet at the farm.
(I will continue my entry when I come home.)

EDITORIAL NOTE:
Jan's diary ends here. No further entry was made, and a long time elapsed before Jan told his story. Here it is.

It was half past seven when Piet and I set out with a truckload of milk for a depot forty miles to the south. After traveling for fifty minutes, we stopped to give a lift to an elderly, stooped hitch-hiker, who looked like a farmer's laborer, and who carried his farming implements.

"Thank you, Jan, thank you, Piet," he murmured as he climbed aboard. "You are right on time." It was Farmer Smit, and we gave him the necessary papers obtained for us by Charlotte. (Charlotte was really marvelous.) He was now Hendrik Buren, with a permit to travel as an itinerant farm laborer.

After twenty minutes we were stopped at a road barrier by a number of German soldiers, headed by a sergeant. He examined all our papers, which were in order, but he was inquisitive about the laborer. "They are kind young men," said the laborer in a weak, trembling voice. "They saw me tired out. I have walked a lot. They even gave me some milk to drink."

"Did they?" said the sergeant. "That's forbidden!"

"Nobody's going to miss a cup from this load," laughed Piet.

"Would you like a little milk?" I whispered to the sergeant. "It won't be missed."

"Some fresh cow's milk would be a welcome change," said the sergeant, and he produced three large tin mugs, which Piet filled to the brim.

Everybody was happy, as off we drove into the night.

After thirty minutes, Farmer Smit took the wheel.

"This is where we turn off toward the river, and it's a bit tricky, because we take a secondary road. It's a pity it's bright moonlight, but that can't be helped."

Twenty-five minutes later we pulled up outside a monastery. Farmer Smit got down.

"There is a convent half a mile down the road. Deliver six churns there, and then unload the rest here. I am going inside."

We carried out the farmer's instructions, and having enjoyed the hospitality of the monks, we were about to start for home when two monks came out, carrying fishing tackle. We were certainly surprised. "We catch good fish by moonlight," said one monk. "Remember that. I hope you will hear it again."

The other monk came close to us. He was Farmer Smit. We could not help laughing.

"Good-bye, Jan, good-bye, Piet. Thank you for everything; especially thank Charlotte. Long live the SS5. If God is good to me,. we will meet again. Look after the farm, if you can. We will need it when I return. And now for some fishing in the Rhine, then in the Meuse, and who knows? God bless you all, and our dear country."

Piet and I had heard of the escape route across the Rhine, then across the Meuse, and then, with the help of the Resistance, through Belgium and on to England.

"Good-bye and good luck," we said, "don't worry, we'll look after the farm for you. We'll keep it in tip-top shape. Meanwhile we hope you will catch good fish by moonlight."

We waited until the two monks had got into their little boat, and had rowed some distance from the shore. Then we started for home.

As it turned out, it was a rash promise that we had made to our farmer friend.

We arrived at the farm at two o'clock in the morning. Everything appeared silent and still. We had barely put the truck away when we were surrounded by armed German soldiers.

We were hauled into the kitchen, to face a member of the dreaded Gestapo. Beside him, with an evil smile on his fat face, stood Klaus the Rat, in full Nazi uniform, and on either side of the officer was a Gestapo subordinate.

Immediately thoughts flashed through my mind. Had we underrated the Rat? Had we been indiscreet in the class, and made fun of the Germans?

"Are these the boys?" the Gestapo officer asked Klaus.

"Yes, sir," came the prompt answer. "They are the traitors."

"Where's Farmer Smit?" asked the Nazi.

"Farmer Smit?" I echoed with surprise. "How should we know? He was here when we left to deliver the milk."

"That's a lie," he stormed, "he was with you."

"Oh no, sir," said Piet innocently, "he was not. Jan and I left alone. I swear to it."

"What's the word of a Dutch traitor worth?" came the sneering reply. "Where did you leave him?"

"We don't know what you're talking about, sir," I began, but a storm of abuse halted me.

"Don't be impertinent, you Dutch swine, or you'll get a dose of treatment that will mark you for life."

He had worked himself up into a fine temper. He wiped the perspiration from his forehead, but suddenly his mood and his tone changed. He sounded almost kind.

"Now, be sensible boys and nothing will happen to you. In fact, there might be a nice reward for you both."

There was a moment's silence, and then Piet spoke. "Please, sir, may we go home? We've had a hard night, and we've got to go to school in the morning."

"There will be no school for you in the morning, or ever again," shrieked the Gestapo officer. He turned to his subordinates. "Take them to my headquarters. We've got ways to make them talk. They'll open their mouths. I'll see to that."

But we did not open our mouths.

I need not detail the refinements of torture practiced by the Gestapo. We had read in school about the Spanish Inquisition in medieval times, and we had heard stories about Nazi torture. We always believed that they could not possibly be true, that a human being could treat another in such a manner.

We were soon disillusioned. I did not know that one could faint into unconsciousness with pain. Sometimes I wondered if I were living.

The souvenirs of the period are a permanent limp for Piet, and a useless left arm for myself, but they were minor injuries. The Gestapo tried their usual tricks on us. They came into my ghastly cell one morning, full of the joy of life.

"Your friend has confessed at last. Now you can give us a full confession without disturbing your conscience."

I knew they were lying, because I know my friend Piet.

"In that case," I said, "you don't have to worry about me, because I have nothing to confess. I didn't even know that he had."

The same routine was tried on Piet, with a like result.

Then, one day, they tried another brutal trick. They told me what would happen to my mother if I did not confess, and they told her what would happen to me if she did not persuade me to do as they wanted.

So one day they dragged me from my cell, and propped me up in a chair, to meet my mother. A Gestapo officer stood in the corner of the room, smoking a cigar.

Tears were streaming down my mother's face as she sat opposite me. She was not allowed to touch me.

"No whispering," shouted the officer. "Speak up clearly."

"What have they done to you, Jan?" said my mother, between sobs, "Your teeth . . ."

They had broken my front teeth.

"The inhuman beasts . . ." I began.

"Don't say that," said my mother.

"You had better not," interjected the Nazi.

"Jan, my darling, why do you suffer so, and make me suffer too? Tell your questioners what they want to know. They have promised me that you will be allowed to come home. I could nurse you back to health. You would like that, wouldn't you? You would soon be your old self again, and I would be spared the nightmares I have. Think it over, my son, for my sake."

The Nazi looked at his wristwatch.

"Time up," he commanded.

"May I kiss my son?" pleaded my mother.

"Make it quick, keep your arms to your side," and he turned his back on us, obviously not wishing to see any sign of love or affection.

My mother kissed me, and whispered hurriedly, "Be brave— keep silent if you can stand it. Father sends his love."

A similar scene took place between Piet and Charlotte, with the same result.

Piet and I were hauled before a military court. The Prosecutor asked us, "Who told you to do these things?"

"We haven't done anything," we both answered, and Piet added, "if we had done anything, we would have acted on our own free will. We are old enough to have our own convictions."

"A pity you're not old enough to face a firing squad," snarled the

Prosecutor. Even the Nazis balked at executing anybody under sixteen years of age. We were sentenced to four years' imprisonment.

Our SS5 had now become the SS3, but they carried on their work of sabotage and risked deportation, and now, because of their age, they risked death. Jos and Hendrik even prepared a plan to set fire to the prison, in order to rescue us. But Charlotte persuaded them not to try it.

The tide was turning and the Nazis in their desperation were killing hundreds of innocent people on the slightest provocation. Some of the warders were becoming kinder, and one of them, bribed by Hendrik, brought us what he thought was a stupid message.

"The doctor said that we catch good fish by moonlight."

Piet and I knew that not only had Farmer Smit arrived safely in London, but that he had also met my father.

Charlotte, Hendrik, and Jos, crouched over the radio, heard Radio Orange, "the voice of the fighting Netherlands," give the news that the Allies had occupied Brussels, and that the Allied troops were moving to the Dutch frontier.

But it was not until the twenty-fourth of March, 1945, that the SS3 heard the news from London that the Allied armies had crossed the Rhine in four different places between Nijmegen and Cologne.

The beginning of the end had really come.

When the first Allied troops swept into Amsterdam, on the eighth of May, 1945—they were Canadians—my father and Farmer Smit were in the vanguard. How they got mixed up with the Canadians neither I nor they ever discovered.

All Dutch political prisoners put in jail by the Nazis were freed. What scenes! What joy and tears of happiness.

After being united with our families, we spent the evening at the crumbling and plundered farm of Farmer Smit, who toasted us, "To the SS5. May their spirit endure forever."

A FOOTNOTE:

In 1950, Princess Margriet, accompanied by her mother, Queen Juliana, unveiled a memorial at Spaarndam, to the courage of Dutch Youth through the ages.

THE YOUNG FALCONS FLY

"LONG LIVE the Czech . . . !"

The last word of the triumphant cry, "People," was never uttered.

It was smothered by a fusilade from German machine guns.

So died the student L.V., after bestial torture, for refusing to give away the hiding place of his friend Jan S——, for whom the Gestapo had offered a reward of 100,000 crowns.

From the fifteenth of March, 1939, a historic date for Europe, when the German Nazi armies marched into Prague, the capital of Czechoslovakia, the ideals of humanity, freedom, toleration, the respect for the individual, all guaranteed by the Czechoslovak State, were destroyed by Hitler's barbarism.

Betrayed by their Western Allies, spoken of by a British Prime Minister, Neville Chamberlain, as "a far-away country," of which so little was known, Czechoslovakia had been forced to deprive the Western Powers of 45 fully equipped divisions, 1,000 tanks, over 1,500 planes, backed by the second strongest armament industry in Europe, and to abandon, as Churchill put it, "frontiers given by God."

Winston Churchill's warnings were heeded by few. After Munich, he told the House of Commons, "All is over. Silent, mournful, abandoned, broken, Czechoslovakia recedes in darkness. The terrible words for the first time have been pronounced against the Western democracies, 'Thou art weighed in the balance and found wanting. . . .' Czechoslovakia will be engulfed by the Nazi regime."

His prophecy came true. The Nazis occupied the country, but they could not conquer the soul of the nation. The people held fast to the saying of their fifteenth-century hero, Jan Hus, "Love the Truth, defend the Truth, speak the Truth, hear the Truth."

Small wonder that the Czech people were filled with hate against their oppressors; but they were also filled with hope. From the smallest child, who wrote chain letters against the Nazis, to the oldest gray-bearded man, they did what they could to show their hatred of the Nazis, and to offer resistance to them. When German newsreels were shown in cinemas, the audience laughed at the Nazi heroics. When uniformed soldiers entered restaurants, the natives walked out. German posters were smothered at night with mud or paint. "Look out! Stolen!" was the slogan daubed on German trucks.

Although it meant death to listen to foreign radio stations, people listened, and many wrote and printed on leaflets what they had heard. They listened to the voice from London of Jan Masaryk, son of the Liberator and first President of their country.

What Hitler described as the obstinacy of the Czech people infuriated him. There were not enough executions. He replaced the Reich Protector, Baron von Neurath, by the "Hangman," Reinhard Heydrich. He appeared in Prague on the twenty-seventh of September, 1941, the eve of the feast of Good King Wenceslaus, the patron saint of Bohemia. He began his career by executing eighty-six people in three days. In one week six thousand people were arrested. His pet hatred were the students and young people. He dissolved the Sokol, that vast gymnastic organization of a million members of both sexes, that had given pride and prestige to Czechoslovakia, and was the admiration of the civilized world.

But these men and women, boys and girls, who had been closely knit in a bond of brotherhood and sisterhood, kept their links, even though they now appeared invisible.

Toward the end of 1941, Heydrich turned his attention to education. All universities, colleges, high schools, polytechnics, all centers of higher education, were closed for three years.

"This is the last class I will take in this Polytechnic."

The teacher, Max K——, faced his sad, silent class.

"Those of you who have taken French will be familiar with *The Last Lesson* by Alphonse Daudet. I have not, like the teacher in *The Last Lesson,* put on my fine Sunday clothes for this sad occasion, but, like him, I say that our language is the loveliest tongue in the world. We must keep it safe and never forget it. So long as we hold firmly to our own mother tongue, we hold the key to our prison. You have all read the order closing us, and other centers of education, for three years. Alas, you are all too old to go back to the primary schools that will remain open."

The teacher managed a faint smile at this, as did some of his pupils.

"This is not the place for me to say good-bye, so I would be honored if all of you would come to coffee at my house on Sunday next. Shall we say at four o'clock?"

Punctually at that hour, the group of twelve—eight boys and four girls—were welcomed by Max and his wife, but they all realized that this was more than a social occasion. An air of solemnity brooded over them all and took the edge off their appetites, as they sat around the festive table, which was a testimony to what a clever housewife could do even in these troubled times.

The hostess realized that she would need to jolly—if not bully—them into eating.

"I hope you're not going to let me down, Kristina," she said laughingly. "That in front of you is a cherry strudel, and the one on the right is a poppy-seed one. Try a piece, and pass them round. I want to see this table cleared, or I shall be very annoyed with you all." That was all the encouragement the boys and girls needed to do justice to the food set before them. The table was cleared.

"Now, Max, if you will take your friends into your study, I can get on with my work," said the hostess.

When they were all comfortably seated in the book-lined room, Max told them the reason for the meeting.

"The time has come for this Resistance Group to break up. You know that those of us who do not find suitable work will be sent to forced labor camps. So I have found jobs for us all, suitable to our talents. You, Florian and Leo, will work in an oil refinery, but you will continue to look after the leaflets and the newspapers. You, Jan, will be an apprentice in an airplane factory, here in Prague, and you, Kristina, will be in the canteen in the same factory. Richard and Liese will work in a munitions factory.

"Jaroslav and Antonin, as natives of Pilsen, you will be employed in the Skoda armament factory, where I, too, will eventually be. Josef and Julius will work on the railway, and Veronika and Irena, you will continue your work in the hospital, full-time now.

"That accounts for you all. These envelopes give you the details of your new employment and the person you have to see there. I'll give them to you before you leave. As you can see, you are all in key places to carry on the sabotage you have done so well. But every precaution must be taken. Sixty thousand Gestapo agents have been sent to our country.

"I am making a little tour, beginning tomorrow, checking up on the links in the chain of our onetime Sokol friends. There's no need for me to remind you that Sokol is the Czech word for falcon, that swift, powerful, fiercely alert bird of nobility, which flies high and strikes with deadly impact.

"I will keep in touch with you all, and those of us who can manage it will meet. Before I forget it, Florian and Leo, here is some copy for your next leaflet. Head it 'A Message from Churchill.' I will read it so that you others will know what it is, 'In this hour of martyrdom, I send you this message. The battle, which we in Britain are fighting today, is not only our battle. It is also your battle. We are both fighting for the fundamental decencies of human life. We have refused to recognize any of the brutal conquests of Germany. Be of good cheer. The hour of your deliverance will come. The soul of freedom is deathless; it cannot, and will not perish.' "

Jan had been crazy about airplanes from early childhood, a passion that baffled his parents, who had no desire to fly anywhere, or, indeed, to leave Prague, which to them was the hub of the universe.

A stroll down the Mala Strana, the ancient picturesque district of Prague, with its palaces, its crooked alleys, its gardens, and then a glass of good Pilsen beer was heaven to these simple people.

Jan's parents had met in a clothing factory, where they were both employed, and where, whenever his mother could spare time from attending to three young schoolchildren, she went, to augment his father's slender wages.

When Jan reported to the airplane factory, he was put in touch with Karel, the works manager. Karel took him on a lightning and fascinating tour of the factory. As they progressed through the various workshops, Karel gave him some good advice.

"I've had a very good report about you from Max, your teacher. See that you live up to it, Jan. You know the old saying 'Speech is silver, silence is gold.' You will remain on the gold standard, that's how I value you"—and he laughed, a nice happy laugh—"and not a mention of your group to anyone. No matter how tempted you will be to speak to any of the workmen, and I emphasize the word 'any,' you will never discuss, or talk, or comment on anything unusual. Is that understood, Jan?"

"Yes, sir."

"You needn't call me sir. You may call me Karel. Come and see me any time you need information or advice. In an emergency, come to my home." He gave him the address. "I am the only one, and I repeat the only one, who may give you orders. And now I will introduce you to Vladimir, at whose bench you will work. He is a good engineer, and you may learn a lot from him."

The introduction over, Karel left Jan with Vladimir, who gave the boy a most hearty welcome.

"Are you fond of planes?" asked Vladimir.

"I'm crazy about planes," replied Jan.

"Have you learned anything about engineering?"

"I studied metallurgy and mechanics."

"Have you now left school?" asked Vladimir.

"My school, the Polytechnic, has been closed," replied Jan.

Vladimir dropped his voice to a whisper, when he asked the next question.

"Don't you hate the Nazis for closing your school?"

"I really haven't thought about it," said Jan. "I suppose I'm sorry in a way, but it means I can earn my living sooner."

"Aren't you sorry to miss your school friends, or do you still meet?"

"Oh, no. We've all got our own jobs now."

Jan found it easy to work with Vladimir. He was patient with the boy, and would explain everything in simple terms; but Jan was amazed at what he considered the indiscretions of Vladimir.

"Aren't they idiots," he said one morning to Jan, "to put the SS men in the factory to watch us? It didn't stop a plane crashing on its trial last week, the third in a month."

Jan was a trifle puzzled. Was Vladimir trying to convey to him that he belonged to a Resistance Group and that any bit of sabotage would be welcome?

"You keep your ears and eyes open," he said on one occasion to Jan, "and you'll see and hear a lot. If there's anything you want to know, just ask me. You and I are a team. We are going to work together."

Jan often saw Kristina in the canteen, but there was no sign of recognition between them. Vladimir always stood behind Jan as they lined up to receive their food, and invariably said the same thing to the girl who was serving. "Give the boy a good portion. He's a growing lad."

It was obvious that Vladimir was quite popular with the girls, and with his co-workers.

Then, one morning, there was a sensation in the factory. The entire factory committee had been arrested. Once again a plane had crashed, the Nazi pilot had been killed, and there was little doubt that it was due to a fault in the machine. This was the fourth crash in five weeks, and the Nazis intended making an example of the leaders, but they reckoned without the Czech workers. They just folded their arms. Not a stroke of work was done.

The managing director was summoned to Petschek Palace, headquarters of the Gestapo, and was grilled by expert Gestapo agents. He maintained that it was not the fault of the planes.

"The German Air Force needs pilots so badly," he said, "that men are allowed to fly new machines earlier than they should. Anyway, what's the use of arresting the entire factory committee, resulting in an idle factory, when planes are needed so badly. If you want to close the factory down, that's the way to do it."

It was a powerful argument, and even the Gestapo could not fail to see the force of it. Back in the factory, the threats of armed SS men had no effect, and Vladimir was one of the principal ringleaders in defying the Nazis. He certainly won the admiration of Jan by the way he stood up to the Nazi bullies.

Not until the committee returned to the factory did a lathe turn, or a man return to his bench.

"That'll teach them a lesson," whispered Vladimir to Jan, who felt quite heroic to have taken part in this act of resistance. That night, Karel and the managing director had a glass of beer together.

"Go slow for a few weeks," said the boss to Karel. "Pass the word round. Perhaps an electrical shortage in one of the shops."

A week later a fire broke out on the floor where Vladimir and Jan were working. How it began was a mystery, but it slowed up work for several days.

"Have you seen anybody around who doesn't belong here?" asked Vladimir of Jan.

"No, nobody," answered Jan.

"Do you think it was sabotage?"

"Oh no," said Jan. "I'm sure it was just an accident. A short circuit or something."

"I wonder," mused Vladimir. "It hits production all right, doesn't it?" and he laughed loudly.

The following morning Jan was given another surprise.

"Have you seen one of these before?" Vladimir asked him, as from an inside pocket he drew out a leaflet, headed "A Message from Churchill." It was the leaflet his group colleagues, Florian and Leo, had set up and distributed.

"Read it," said Vladimir, "it will interest you."

Jan read it, although he almost knew it by heart.

"Why do you keep things like this, Vladimir?" whispered Jan. "It's dangerous. If they found this on you, it could mean death."

"I enjoy defying those swine," said Vladimir, "and I admire the people who do these leaflets. They tell me that students like yourself do these things."

"I've never heard that," said Jan.

Was Vladimir, evidently a member of a Resistance Group, testing him? Was he finding out if he, Jan, could be trusted to keep his mouth shut?

For a fleeting moment he was tempted to boast about his Youth

Resistance Group, then he remembered Karel's warning—"Trust nobody."

Vladimir broke in on Jan's reverie.

"Have you remembered somebody from the Polytechnic? Perhaps one of the teachers?"

"No," answered Jan, "the only time we did anything in class was to draw up a protest about the school meals, but it didn't help," added Jan with a laugh.

"Anyway," concluded Vladimir, "if you run across any information, let me know, because I can give the writers good, useful material."

"I certainly will," said Jan. He felt rather mean about keeping Vladimir in the dark, but a promise must be kept.

There was quiet jubilation in the factory when news reached them that there had been a fire in the Skoda Armament Works in Pilsen, and that a transformer had been destroyed, holding up work for several days.

"Hangman" Heydrich was furious. Since the war with Russia, production had fallen by 30 percent. These results of sabotage so pleased Frantisek, one of the workmen in the plane factory, that he offered to stand drinks to the men working nearest him, and that included Vladimir and Jan.

"We'll enjoy that glass of beer," said Vladimir to Jan when time came to knock off. "Let's get washed quickly and go to the beer cellar."

The two of them went into the washroom to take off some of the factory grime. Vladimir was obviously in a hurry. He almost tore his coat off its hook, and as he did so, his wallet fell on the floor of the washroom, without his noticing it. He had already left the room when Jan saw the wallet. In falling, it had opened, strewing some of its contents on the floor. Jan collected them to put them back.

Imagine his shock, when, in addition to the identity card every workman had to carry, there was also an identity card of Vladimir in the full Nazi uniform of an SS officer. Jan hurriedly put everything into the wallet, closed it, let it lie on the floor, and concluded washing as though nothing had happened, just as Vladimir rushed into the room, almost in panic. He quickly picked it up.

"Dropped my wallet," he said to Jan. "Did you notice it?"

"No, Vladimir, I was taking the dirt out of my eyes."

Vladimir was obviously relieved.

They went to the beer cellar, where the imprudent and overjoyed patriot, Frantisek, stood drinks to all who could drink with him, to the downfall of the Nazi Reich.

Jan was greatly perturbed. Was Vladimir a Gestapo agent? Was he a double agent? It seemed quite likely by the manner in which he enjoyed Frantisek's hospitality, and the way in which he returned it.

In a spirit of bravado, Vladimir produced a beret with its feather, once part of the Sokol uniform, and did a solo dance to the enjoyment and applause of the drinkers. As he flopped into a chair, Vladimir noticed that Jan appeared worried, but he excused himself on the grounds that he was not used to drinking, and that, as he did not want to be a spoilsport, he would slip away home.

"See you in the morning," said Vladimir.

"See you then," responded Jan.

All the way home, Jan argued with himself what was the right thing to do. Should he go to Karel and tell him what he had seen? Would he make a fool of himself, when he learned that Vladimir was one of the most trusted members of the Resistance?

On the other hand, all the questions that Vladimir asked him now had a significance. The bits of puzzle were falling into place. Jan decided to talk it over with Kristina. He called at her home. She had just come back from the factory, and over a cup of coffee Jan told her the story of his relationship with Vladimir, and of his dilemma.

"Let's shadow him for a few days," suggested Kristina. "You won't be of any use, except to fix his identity. I know the man you mean; that tall one, who stands behind you when you come to the canteen for food. Irena is on night duty at the hospital this week. She could do it for a few days. But where could she begin?"

"After the day's work, we nearly always go into the beer cellar next to the factory. Vladimir drinks beer or spirits, I have raspberry juice. We spend about fifteen minutes there."

"Leave it to me," said Kristina. "I'll arrange it all right."

There was gloom in the factory the next morning, particularly in the section in which Jan worked. Frantisek had been arrested during the night and taken by the Gestapo to their HQ, the Petschek Palace. He was the third individual worker to be arrested in the past four weeks, and each victim had been somewhat revolutionary and outspoken about the Nazis.

Vladimir was duly sad, along with his other workmates.

"Frantisek must have been overheard in the beer cellar last night," said Vladimir to Jan. "It's a lesson to us, Jan, to be careful what you say and to whom you say it."

Would a traitor speak like that, thought Jan? Or was it Vladimir who gave away Frantisek? What would happen to the poor fellow? He would be tortured, for certain, and after that he would probably be one more to add to the growing list of those hanged or shot. Already the total since Heydrich's arrival in Prague was running into many hundreds. That night, at the end of the day's work, Vladimir invited Jan to have a drink.

"We need one after today's misery," said Vladimir.

Jan agreed.

They left the beer cellar together, and, as usual, shook hands when they said good night.

Irena witnessed this, and set out to trail Vladimir. She noticed with interest that he behaved as though he were being watched and followed. Fifteen minutes' walk from the factory brought him to the apartment house where he lived. Irena waited for an hour, keeping watch on the entrance, but without anything happening. She reported the result to Kristina.

The same thing happened the next night, and the night after that. On the fourth night, Veronika, being off duty, offered to help Irena. They soon spotted Vladimir and Jan as they said good night, this time at the tram queue. Vladimir decided to take the tram. He said that he was too tired to walk. Veronika managed to stand in front of him, three or four people away, while Irena stationed herself behind him. They wanted to make sure that at least one of them would be with him.

As it happened, both girls were with him in the tram but they sat apart.

Ten minutes later, Vladimir rose to get off. There were quite a number of people alighting, so there was nothing obvious about the two girls getting off at this stop. Irena crossed the road, while Veronika kept to the same side as Vladimir.

It soon became obvious that he was not going home that evening, or, if he was, he was going to take a long, roundabout route. At every corner, and before entering a street, he tried to be casual about seeing if he were being followed, but it never occurred to him that he might be shadowed by two girls.

Finally, he reached his destination. He was opposite the Petschek Palace, HQ of the Gestapo. This time he looked around quite a bit before crossing the road. He lit a cigarette and looked up and down the street. The girls could scarcely contain their excitement as they saw him enter, but what was most significant of all was that two uniformed men on duty outside the entrance saluted him very smartly.

The girls kept watch for thirty minutes, then Veronika went back to her hospital duty, and Irena went as quickly as she could to Jan's home. As an old Sokol "sister," Jan's parents made her welcome. It was just a call to see how her old friend Jan was getting on, and now she must go to the hospital. Jan, of course, would walk with her.

Even after having seen Vladimir's photo in SS uniform, the news that he was *persona grata* at the Gestapo HQ shocked Jan. He decided that he would call on Karel. This was certainly the sort of emergency that merited a visit to Karel's home. Meanwhile, he and the girls would not speak to anybody.

It was with a certain feeling of trepidation that he rang the bell at Karel's apartment, and asked the maid if Mr. S—— were in. At this moment, Mrs. S—— came to the door. In these days a ring at the bell might mean anything. She was prepared for all emergencies. Jan explained who he was, and was greeted very cordially. He was taken into Karel's den. As soon as Karel entered the room, he knew that something was amiss. Jan told his story. Karel did not interrupt once. He listened to every word that Jan spoke. When he had finished, Karel thanked him, and asked him to keep silent about this. It still needed checking. Unlike the Nazis, Karel and his group would want still further proof. But they would move fast.

Two days later, telephone engineers had to check the wires and apparatus in the apartment house where Vladimir lived. They entered Vladimir's home while he was away at the factory, and spent a useful half hour there.

This was on a Friday morning. The following morning, Karel had a recording of a conversation between Vladimir and a Gestapo official, whose anonymity was cloaked by number 012. Vladimir's number was 096.

"I feel that it is time that I moved." That was the gist of Vladimir's telephone conversation.

"I have a feeling that they might be on to me any day. I can't say why, but after the last arrest of Frantisek, a workman from here, they started probing, and they're not fools at it. I suggest that you arrest me next Tuesday at the factory. I'll make a great show of my innocence. Then we can decide where I go next."

There was a slight pause, then, with a laugh, Vladimir said, "I will await you on Tuesday."

Karel had to make a quick decision. He took three of his intimates and Jan into his confidence, and also allotted a key role to Kristina. Monday morning arrived, and there was nothing to indicate that Vladimir had decided that this was to be his last full day in the factory. He was quite jolly, and seemed particularly happy when he gave Jan news of recent sabotage.

"We had a good time last week," he whispered. "There's been a fire in the oil refineries at Kralupy. Machinery and gasoline tanks have been destroyed. There's also been a fire in the munition works of Sellier and Bellot in Vlasim, the filling factory was blown up, and a lot of imported Germans were killed. A reward of ten thousand crowns has been offered, but I don't think that it will ever be claimed."

Just then, Karel, on his usual tour of inspection came to their bench. He was in his usual friendly mood.

"Hello, Vladimir, how's everything?"

"Fine, Karel. I was just giving Jan good news about sabotage. I hear there's been a strike in the mines, just when the blast furnaces need charging. That means at least forty-eight hours to restart a blast furnace once it goes out."

"I wouldn't know," said Karel, "I have my own worries here. How's the boy behaving?"

"Oh, Jan," replied Vladimir, "he's a very willing learner. He'll make a good engineer."

"Keep it up, Jan," said Karel as he moved on.

❋

There was the usual line in the canteen for the midday meal. Vladimir stood behind Jan, and Kristina served them. Vladimir cracked his usual gag. "Give the boy an extra dumpling. He's a growing lad."

Kristina ignored them both, and carried on filling the bowls with soup, and the plates with what outsiders called "privileged workers' food."

Vladimir and Jan sat at a table, and ate their meal with good appetites.

"I'll get the coffee," said Jan, and once again Kristina served him.

The meal break over, the men trooped back to their work benches. After about fifteen minutes, Vladimir sat down heavily on his stool, and passed his hand wearily across his forehead.

"I don't feel well," he muttered to Jan. "I can hardly keep my eyes open."

"I hope it isn't flu," said a concerned Jan. "There is a lot of it around. Shall I walk with you to the doctor?"

"No," replied Vladimir, "I'll be all right in a minute."

Two minutes later, he was sprawled across the bench, fast asleep. Kristina had done her part very well.

When Vladimir awoke, he discovered that he was in a cellar, propped up at a table, facing Karel and five other workmen. On the table was his identity card as an SS officer, and the tape recording of his telephone conversation.

Without saying a word, Karel put the tape on the machine and played back the conversation. Vladimir laughed, but it was an uneasy laugh. He had more than once visualized such a situation, and had always told himself that he would be able to bluff his way out.

"That's quite right," he said, "that is my voice, and that is my picture, but I'm a double agent. My first allegiance is to this country, I am a patriotic Czech. I belong to the highest Resistance Group in this country. I am forbidden to name it, even at the cost of my life."

"A very pretty speech, 096," interrupted Karel. "That would account for Frantisek being shot, for Thomas being hanged, and for twenty others being sent to concentration camps. We have been piecing things together like a jigsaw puzzle, and the final picture points to you. Shall we tell you of your past association with 'Executioner' Heydrich? Shall we tell you of the time you spent with that bloody swine Karl Herman Frank, when you both sold postcards in Karlovy Vary? I see you've gone pale. Your one life can't atone for the many innocent people you have killed, but at least one more Nazi will get his just deserts. Vladimir D——, you have been sentenced to death, and if you feel like saying 'Heil Hitler,' you are welcome to it."

Tuesday morning was awaited with some apprehension by the managing director of the factory, and by those workers in the know. Jan duly reported to his foreman the absence of Vladimir, and was assigned to another worker.

Precisely at eleven o'clock in the morning, two Gestapo officers, accompanied by four SS men, arrived at the plane factory. The Gestapo officers were taken to the Board Room, and having shown their credentials, they were welcomed by the managing director.

"What can I do for you, gentlemen?"

"We wish to see one of your workers, Vladimir D——."

"Do you know which department he is in?"

"We do not."

The managing director spoke on the intercom, and discovered that Vladimir D—— was in the engine section. Again he spoke on the intercom.

"Is that you, Edouard? Please send one of your men, Vladimir D——, to the Board Room. Tell him how to get here."

Back came the reply. "He is not here this morning. The apprentice, Jan, who works with him, reported his absence and said that Vladimir was not well yesterday afternoon. It looked like flu."

"Ask the apprentice to come here," interpolated a Gestapo officer.

"Send the apprentice, Jan, to the Board Room. Show him the way."

A few minutes later a timid knock on the door heralded the arrival and the entry of Jan.

"Come in, Jan," said the managing director kindly. "Sit down. These gentlemen may want to ask you some questions."

One of the Gestapo men showed Jan a photograph—just a large head—of Vladimir.

"Is that the man you work with?"

Jan's eyes shone with delight, and he was most enthusiastic.

"Oh yes, that is Vladimir. I've been working with him since I became an apprentice here. He's very kind to me, and very patient, especially when I ask a foolish question. He's a fine technician, if it's not too presumptuous of me to say so. I learn a lot from him."

Then came the anxious question from Jan. "Has something happened to him?"

"No, no," said a Gestapo officer hurriedly. "You told your foreman this morning that Vladimir was not well yesterday."

"Yes, sir," said Jan. "He complained all day about a headache, and aches in his bones, and being hot and cold. I suggested that he should see the doctor, but he said that after a good hot drink, some aspirin, and a good sleep, he would be as right as rain in the morning. 'I mustn't hold up production,' he said, 'I must be at my bench in the morning.' I said that he ought to have a few days' rest, because he is such a hard worker. Then he said, 'Jan, have you ever been to Salzburg?' I said, 'No, Vladimir, I could never afford to go out of the country.' 'We must have a holiday there soon,' he said. 'You and I, Jan.' I said I would like that. Then, at the end of the day, we missed going into the beer cellar for the usual drink. 'I'm too tired,' he said. He said, 'See you in the morning,' and I said, 'I hope you'll be better then.' He said 'Thank you,' and off he went."

A Gestapo officer turned to the managing director.

"Have you made inquiries at the man's home?"

"We don't usually do so on the first day of an illness. We do after the second day."

"Good," replied the officer, "we may be seeing you again."

The following afternoon the managing director was anxiously pacing up and down his office. At last came the knock on the door for which he was waiting, and the entrance of Karel.

"You want to see me? I'm sorry I was so long at our sub-factory . . ."

"Never mind that," came the hurried interruption. "Don't sit down, Karel, there's no time. This is good-bye to Prague for you, and to Czechoslovakia for the time being. My contact at the Gestapo has been on to me—yes, Karel, where patriotism is not strong enough, money is—the Gestapo have an idea about what might have happened to Vladimir and he obviously left them your name at some time. You have been marked down. I've put 'Operation Exit,' into motion. The Youth Resistance Group will work it. Your wife is already on her way to the Hungarian frontier. The children are in the hospital—no, don't get excited. There's nothing wrong, our ex-Sokol nurses are in charge. We couldn't wait for you to get back from the factory, and, in any case, there was no time for any good-byes to your family.

"This is what you have to do. Go into my bathroom there, and shave off your moustache. Yes, I know how proud you are of it, but off it comes. Every border has instructions to look out for you, with or without a woman and two children. Take this,"—and he handed Karel an envelope stuffed with money. "When you've shaved—do it quickly—go to Charles Bridge and stand by the statue of St. Christopher. Our contact will ask you if this is the old 'Stone Bridge,' and you will answer that it is, and that it is also the Charles Bridge, and that it is 520 meters long and 10 meters wide. Also that it has thirty statues. Then do as the boy says."

Just then a message came through on the intercom from the managing director's secretary.

"Two gentlemen have arrived to see you, sir."

"Show them into the Board Room, and then have me paged in the factory."

He turned to Karel.

"Sooner than I thought. Good-bye. I'll lock the door of the washroom. Use the door to my private elevator. Go down to the basement, and out through the back entrance. You know the way. I'll find some method of keeping in touch. No thanks, please." He opened the door of the washroom, pushed Karel in, locked the door, pocketed the key, and went down into the factory.

There he saw Karel's deputy, and explained the situation.

After being paged for a convenient period, the managing director asked on the intercom why he was wanted. He was informed that two gentlemen were waiting to see him in the Board Room.

"I'm sorry if there has been any delay," he said as he hurriedly entered the room, "but I have been on my usual tour of inspection. One must show the workers that you take an interest in what's being done. Will you gentlemen join me in coffee? I always have it at this time of the afternoon."

Without waiting for a reply, he ordered coffee for three to be brought to the Board Room.

"Now, gentlemen, I am at your disposal."

One of the two Gestapo officers handed him a slip of paper with Karel's name on it.

"We would like to see this man."

"Certainly," replied the managing director, "he is my works manager." And with concern he asked, "Is there any trouble?"

There was no reply.

He pressed a button on the intercom and spoke. The answers were very audible.

"Karel?"

"No, sir, this is Vaclav."

"I want to speak to Karel."

"He's not here, sir. He hasn't returned yet."

"Returned from where?" asked the managing director. He was becoming annoyed.

"From our sub-factory, sir. He was becoming worried about the quality of some of the work, and he decided to do some plain talking. But he should be back within an hour or so."

"Thank you, Vaclav. If you see Karel before I do, ask him to see me."

"Yes, sir, I will."

He turned to the Gestapo officers, "You heard the conversation, gentlemen. Our sub-factory is, alas, ten miles away, but it is a very important subsidiary. They manufacture lots of spare parts."

The managing director's secretary arrived with the coffee, and did the pouring out before she left.

"Will you wait for this man here, or would you care to tour the factory until he returns?"

They decided to tour the factory.

Through tear-dimmed eyes, Karel looked at the skyline of the Golden City of Prague, the city of his birth and the town he adored above all others in the world. Was it really a German—Goethe— who called Prague "the most beautiful jewel in the stone crown of the globe?" A lifetime of intimacy with the city had not lessened the rapture with which he looked at the Castle, the heart of Prague, and at St. Vitus' Cathedral, an inseparable part of the outline of the Castle.

How often, as a lad, had he been taken by his father into the many chapels of the Cathedral, and he recalled how he had given rein to his fantasy when he looked at the sixteen houses, built into the castle wall, of "Gold Lane," where the alchemists were said to have lived and experimented.

He remembered how proud he was to have been offered a place in Prague University, and how rich his cultural life had been. It was on the very bridge where he was now standing that, at the age of three, his father had shown him the statues, and that at the age of six, he could reel off the names of all the thirty statues which adorn the bridge.

He looked into the waters of the Vltava, the river on which Prague stands, and whose waters, he could not help thinking, would keep the secret of Vladimir's cement-weighted body for many a day. How often had he and his wife, Vera, walked across this bridge. Would they ever do so again?

A boy of sixteen was tugging his sleeve.

"Excuse me, sir, is this the Old Stone bridge?"

"It is, but it is also Charles Bridge. It is 520 meters long and 10 meters wide. Also it has thirty statues."

"Please come with me," said the boy, and led the way.

Neither spoke, but Karel wondered, as he walked through the familiar squares and the alleys, whether he would ever see his "city of a hundred towers and spires" again, and if, and when, he would be reunited with his family. His safety, indeed his life, was in the hands of boys and girls, members of a Resistance Group, like the confident boy now leading the way.

They entered a small photographic studio. His hair was parted differently and without any preliminaries a passport picture was taken of Karel. "Your wife was here this morning," said the photographer.

Soon the picture was developed and printed, and one found its way into the passport of Leo A——, the new name Karel had been given. His identity papers in the new name showed that he was employed at the plane works, and, indeed Leo A—— was on the roll of the woodworking department and had been given sick leave, should anybody inquire. His old papers were destroyed by fire.

"You may not recognize the Prague address on your papers. You are a lodger with Kristina's parents. It has all been arranged."

He was given a letter from the doctor of the plane factory, to a doctor in Piestany Spa saying that Leo A—— needed treatment for acute arthritis and for rehabilitation. He had full permission from the necessary authorities to spend the requisite time in the spa, when he should be fit to return to work. To his great surprise, a small suitcase—his own—which had been packed by his wife in the morning, was given to him. Every identity had been removed from the suit and underwear. Karel—now Leo—could not help laughing.

"You've certainly been very thorough."

"We have to be," said the boy who had met him on the bridge, "your life depends on it."

Final instructions were given to Karel. "You take the train to Jihlava. When you arrive there, you wait until the platform is cleared a bit. Then you remove your hat and wipe your brow with your handkerchief. You do that until you are approached by the contact there. He will say, 'A falcon is trained to hawk for sport,' and you will answer, 'As Shakespeare said, "a falcon towering in her pride of place." ' He will then take charge. Good-bye and good luck, until we meet again on the day of victory, which will surely come."

While Karel was on his way to Piestany, his wife, Vera, with new identity papers, was on her way to Pardubice. Her papers, signed by the Minister of Commerce, identified her as a businesswoman, unmarried, and a sales representative of textile and silk manufacturers in the ancient town of Zabreh. Her passport gave evidence of transactions in Germany, Austria, Hungary, and Poland. Once again there was evidence that money could be well spent by bribing the right people.

When she arrived at the station of Pardubice, a town that was always proud of its cultural institutions, she put her suitcase down on the platform, and consulted what appeared to be a timetable.

Actually, her thoughts were far away. She remembered how, when she and her husband were students at Prague University, they often came to this very station, as the starting point for their excursions. It was on the top of Mount Kunetice, the high sugarloaf hill, by the fifteenth-century castle, that Karel had proposed to her.

"Papers!" The strident command by an SS soldier soon brought Vera back to everyday reality. She opened her bag and handed over her identity papers and her passport.

At this moment, a fifteen-year-old girl came tearing along the platform, clutching a bunch of wild flowers.

"Oh, Auntie, I am so sorry I am late," she said, and they kissed.

The papers obviously impressed the SS man, who handed them back, saluted, and departed.

"I'm late because we had to decode a message that had just come. It was for you."

Vera laughed. "How do you know I am who I am supposed to be?"

She picked up Vera's case and joined in the laughter, as they walked along the platform. "Instinct," she said. "These flowers are for you."

"At least, the Nazis can't stop those from growing," answered Vera, and they both laughed, because those two phrases were the passwords.

"By the way," said the girl, "my name's Rosa."

"And mine's Vera. The message, please?" said Vera, who was scared what it might be.

"So far everything is most satisfactory. Will keep you informed."

There were tears in her eyes and in her voice as Vera thanked the girl.

"You are staying with us until word comes from our group in Zabreh that all is well. Probably the day after tomorrow."

The day spent with Rosa, her family, and some of the members of the group, was one to remember all her life. Their kindness and their thoughtfulness were most touching. And their courage in risking torture and death to defy the Nazis and to sabotage their war effort, was beyond praise.

On the second day, a boy from Zabreh came to Rosa's house. He reported to Vera.

"I am Thomas, an apprentice in the textile factory which you represent, and on our way to Zabreh I will give you, to the best of my ability, an account of the work we do and the sort of textiles we make. If you are ready, we can leave now."

With a promise to return to Pardubice when victory was won, Vera said good-bye to her new friends and set out by train with Thomas for Zabreh. The journey was, fortunately, uneventful, and it was outside the ancient house where Comenius used to live that Thomas handed Vera over to a chauffeur and a car. It was significant that the home of the seventeenth-century philosopher and theologian, who had been persecuted and driven from his country, should have been selected as a rendezvous. In the car was a case containing samples, prices, etc., from the textile factory.

"We are off to Bratislava," volunteered the chauffeur. "You just say, Madam, when you are hungry, and I'll pull up. I would suggest Kromeriz. There's a very nice restaurant and they know me well, which makes a lot of difference these days, believe me."

"How right you are," agreed Vera.

The chauffeur kept up a running monologue all the way to Kromeriz, but there was much sound sense in all he said.

There was no doubt that he was a favorite at the restaurant. Vera had forgotten that such table delicacies had ever existed. The chauffeur's comment was, "After all, one must live, even though the Nazis poison the air."

The journey took them to Bratislava, where the chauffeur pulled up outside a large department store. "This is where I leave you," said the chauffeur, "but first I'll carry your cases inside."

"Are you married?" asked Vera.

"And how!" came the laughing reply. "Only a wife and five daughters!"

"Would you be annoyed if I bought a little gift for each of them? Say, for example, a scarf."

"Forget it, Madam. When this nasty business is all over, come back to Zabreh and buy me a drink."

"That's a promise," said Vera.

"Follow me," and Vera entered the store with the chauffeur, who asked for Mrs. D——.

"Yes, she is expecting us," was the chauffeur's quick reply to the usual question.

They were shown into an office, where a smart, middle-aged woman was examining samples.

"Good-bye," boomed the chauffeur.

"Good-bye, Antonin," said the woman, "and thank you. My

love to your family." She dismissed the assistant who was with her and then welcomed Vera.

"I've been expecting you. I'm Maria. We had better open your samples, as a necessary precaution." This was done. "I've a message for you. All is well. Your husband is not far away, and your children are well."

She did not dare to tell Vera that her husband was no great distance away in Piestany. It might complicate matters. Vera was very controlled when she thanked Maria.

"You will be staying with me until you move on. As head buyer, it is not unusual for me to give hospitality to a representative of a valued company. Staying at a hotel these days involves too much red tape."

She rang for Mr. George. In came a grizzled old man. She introduced Vera.

"This is the lady about whom I spoke to you. What's the present position?"

"Hopeless," came the answer. "The Gestapo's buzzing round the frontier like wasps round a honeypot. They're after somebody. I'll check again tomorrow. I'll make a trial run. In any case, our man won't be on day duty until three days' time. He says that they are on the special lookout for a man and a woman with two children. We don't want to cross at night. Too suspicious."

"Thank you, George. Keep me informed." She then turned to Vera. "Do you know Bratislava?"

"Not very well."

"Good, then my son Rudolf can have a field day. It will remind him of the excursions he made with his school friends. You will get a good view beyond the Danube of Austria and Hungary from the top of the old Castle. Anyway, you have to stay in Bratislava—if anyone is nosy enough to inquire—because the head buyer of this firm—that's me—cannot make up her stupid mind what textiles to order . . . and now let's go home."

So wonderful had been the hospitality in Bratislava that in a sense Vera was sorry when George reported that the frontier station had now returned to normal for a day or two.

"Rudolf will travel with you in the train as far as Komarno," said Maria, and in Vera's order book she wrote the name of the store and of the buyer, Vera's contact in Budapest. The train journey was uninterrupted. At the frontier, as predicted, the official who checked Vera's papers was most considerate.

"This is where I leave you," said Rudolf. "This is as far as the falcon flies. But our friends on the other side will take great care of you. Here's the number of the car waiting for you. Good-bye and good luck. Until we meet again, which I hope will be soon."

"Thank you for your kindness, Rudolf. Without you and your young falcon brothers and sisters, I don't know what would have happened to us. God bless you all."

Within a few hours, Vera was established in an apartment in Budapest, waiting to be reunited with Karel and the children.

Leo—Karel kept repeating his new name to familiarize himself with it—traveled to Jihlava by train without a question being asked. He was met, as arranged, by a member of the Youth Resistance Group, spent the night in his house, and set off in the morning for Piestany Spa, from where the all clear had arrived. He was to repeat the same action and password as he had done on Jihlava Station.

He had barely stepped onto the platform at Piestany, removed his hat and wiped his brow, when a girl of about sixteen took him by the hand, and walked quickly with him to the end of the platform.

"Don't ask any questions," she murmured, "just follow me. Cross the lines here, behind the train. My name is Lucia. I know yours." She then led him to a passage alongside the station and out into the street, where a cab was waiting. Karel followed her into the cab, which then drove off.

"I was to have taken you to the doctor, but that plan is off. He was arrested this morning, so we couldn't inform you in Jihlava. The Gestapo have taken charge of his clinic and are screening every patient. Somebody must have given him away. He was the head of our group and has been doing wonderful work. You will stay in my home until tomorrow, when we'll move to the frontier, if the coast is clear. If not, you stay put." Karel was amazed at the commanding confidence of the girl.

The cab pulled up at a corner of a street. "We get out here," said the girl, "and walk for a few minutes. A cab outside our house would raise some eyebrows."

She then turned to the driver and suggested that he go to Nitra for the latest report. Once again, Karel was to experience the warm hospitality of simple people, who were willing to risk their lives to help defeat the Nazis. But an hour later, the cab driver knocked on Lucia's door. The Gestapo were making a quick sweep through many houses. They might be here within the hour.

"Can you ride a bicycle?" asked Lucia.

"Of course," answered Karel.

Within minutes they were on their way to a farm, five miles away. That night Karel's bed was in a hayloft.

The next morning the cab driver reported that conditions were favorable. Lucia collected Karel and advised him to leave his suitcase and the clothes in the house, so that he could move more freely.

"Claim them when this is all over," said his host, and refused to take the money Karel so gladly offered him.

The girl, wearing an old raincoat, led Karel to the outskirts of the spa, before the cab picked them up to take them to Nitra. The cab driver and Karel began their noon meal, while the girl went to her contact to check the latest information. When she joined them, she had decided where the crossing would be—a spot with which she was very familiar.

That afternoon the cab took Lucia and Karel to Levice, where the cab would wait, until the girl had completed her mission. The driver was particularly happy with the money Karel slipped him.

In Levice, a farm cart driven by a young lad was waiting to take them as near the frontier as was considered safe.

"I'll wait for you at the usual place, Lucia," said the boy, when Karel and the girl got down.

"We must cross before the moon rises," said the girl.

"How do you mean, 'we'?" asked Karel. "You don't have to come with me. Just show me the way."

For the first time since he left Prague, Karel felt nervous. He knew that if he was caught, he would get short shrift. It was the girl he was worried about. She sensed this.

"Don't worry about me," she laughed. "I have done this seventeen times at various crossings."

Night had fallen when they arrived at her chosen spot.

"You lie down here," she said to Karel, "until I return."

From her pocket she took a bottle and poured out a liquid, a drop at a time, covering an area of about a mile. She returned twenty minutes later, much to Karel's relief.

"Right, let's move," she said, and walked in the opposite direction. "In case they use dogs, the scent I've just laid will lead them nicely into the Danube."

They walked for an hour before she gave the order to lie down beneath a black poplar. "This is my favorite tree," she said, "and from now on, no speaking."

Faintly, through the stillness of the night, came the baying of the dogs, but in decreasing volume of sound. Lucia put on a pair of old leather gloves, and looked at the luminous dial of her wristwatch. After a pause of two minutes, which seemed an interminable silence to Karel, who kept wondering if the Alsatian dogs had really been fooled, she took out a rubber whistle from her pocket—used by bird hunters as a decoy—and blew on it the cry of a wild duck. It echoed through the silent night, but there was no response.

"He must have been held up," she murmured, and added, "be patient," as she touched Karel's arm. It was easy to give advice, thought Karel, but through his mind flashed every kind of horrible happening. He did not much mind for himself, if only he could be sure that his wife and children were safe.

Five more interminable minutes passed, and once again the call of the wild duck pierced the night air. This time an answering call came back.

"Good," muttered Lucia, "I'm going to cut two strands of barbed wire, enough for us to crawl through. Try not to get caught on it. Then wriggle along behind me. Don't cry out or scream if any live thing runs across us, or if we flop in water. It's very shallow. Follow me."

They wriggled along to the barbed wire, which Lucia cut expertly, making a gap just wide enough for them to crawl through. She motioned to Karel to lie still. After a slight pause to make sure that all was well, she inched forward very slowly, so quietly and slowly that she did not even disturb the nest of a wild fowl.

Suddenly a low pinpoint of light appeared for one second, but Lucia had seen it. She moved her body round half left, and propelled herself almost silently to the spot where she had seen the light. Karel followed as best he could, marveling at the agility of this girl.

Then came the whispered word, "Here," and Karel's arm was gripped, and he was literally pulled through a gap in the barbed wire.

"Good-bye and good luck," murmured Lucia, and was already on her way back.

"You're not . . ." began Karel, but he never finished the sentence. She had already disappeared. Karel could not help thinking how right Nature was when she made the female falcon bolder than the male.

"Welcome to Hungary," said a young man of about eighteen. "This way."

He led Karel to a lane where he had left his motorbike.

"I'm afraid you'll have to ride pillion, but not for long. You're spending the night with some friends in Vac. Tomorrow I will take you the twenty-one miles to Budapest."

When Karel started out the next morning for Budapest, his papers identified him as a motor engineer, working at a Budapest garage.

By noon he was reunited with his wife, Vera.

Two hours after Vera had been established in the apartment in Budapest, a message had been received by Irena and Veronika that the way was clear for Karel and Vera's children to be brought to Budapest.

With the material assistance of the managing director of the plane factory, papers were obtained stating that the children, two girls aged three years and eighteen months, whose parents were killed in an accident, were to be allowed to be taken to Budapest, where their maternal grandparents lived. The papers were given by Jan to Veronika at the hospital, an errand which filled him with joy.

By the following morning, all arrangements were made by Karel's former boss for Veronika to escort the children to Budapest. It would be impolite and indelicate to intrude on the reception the children and Veronika had when the Prague to Budapest train halted in the Hungarian capital.

❋

The call had come from Max for those of the group who could manage to meet on Sunday in the ancient town of Beroun. Only two were absent from the rendezvous. Julius was on railway duty, and Liese had to work in the munitions factory.

They made their way to a quiet inn by the river Berounka, where, over a satisying meal, they made their reports to Max.

"First," said Max, "let me report my sad news from the Skoda factory. The barrel of one of our big guns exploded during a firing test. Yaroslav and Antonin can add to that."

"We've had a fire in the factory," said Antonin, "and a transformer was destroyed, holding up work for several days."

"Can you remember these sad events for your newspaper, Florian and Leo?" asked Max.

"We can," they replied in unison. "We, too, had a fire at the oil refinery. Machinery and gasoline tanks were destroyed."

"How about you, Josef?"

"I think we contributed to a record," answered Josef. "The normal time for a goods train from Dresden to Vienna takes three days. We in Prague helped to lengthen the journey to a month."

This brought really broad smiles.

"I think we also helped to pull off a record in our munition factory," said Richard. "The Nazi army returned to us twenty million rounds of small-arms ammunition which were defective."

Jan was silent, even among his own group.

"I know about you, Jan, and you, Kristina, and you too, Veronika, and Irena," said Max. "My congratulations to you all. Try as the Nazis will to clip our wings, the young falcons fly triumphantly, and will, with God's help, continue to do so."

"NOT EVERY GERMAN
IS A NAZI"

BERLIN, March, 1943

A hushed silence came over the living room of architect Manfred
B———, a silence that could have been broken by the dropping of
the proverbial pin. Father was reading, mother was mending socks,
and their fifteen-year-old daughter, Renate, had just made a most
solemn pronouncement.

Both mother and father looked up, shocked and surprised. Father was about to say something, when the silence was shattered by
the wailing siren, warning of an air raid.

"Let's go down to the cellar," said the father, "before the air-
raid warden fetches us. You know how angry he gets. We'll talk
about this when the all clear sounds." Mother collected her socks
and wool. The siren was still shrieking.

"And for this we have to thank our Führer," was the sarcastic
comment of Renate. "When he obliterated the English city of Cov-
entry, he and Goering boasted that no bombers would reach our
towns."

"Please, Renate, no comments," pleaded her mother. "And take
some school books with you."

"And please wear your Hitler Youth badge," added father.

"Must I?" asked the girl.

"You must. And will you please remember that a derogatory remark about the Government can cost you, and us, our lives."

"Yes, Father."

Architect B—— had married late in life, and Renate was their one and only precious child.

Ostensibly, a valued member of the Nazi party—or he could not have held his position—Manfred B—— was employed by the Ministry of Works. He betrayed no interest in politics or racial discrimination, excusing himself by saying that the only things he was competent to talk about were plans for buildings and houses. He and his wife were a quiet sympathetic couple, much respected by their neighbors.

The tenants of the apartment house were hurrying down to the shelter of the communal cellar. All carried pillows and blankets. Some had eiderdowns, and some carried suitcases containing their most precious belongings.

Each of the eight families who lived in the house had its particular part of the cellar, and once settled in, they gave a good imitation of inanimate waxworks. The young children soon fell asleep. Fortunately for them, they had no conscience or thoughts of the future to trouble them.

Occasionally the silence would be broken by a woman—most of them taking shelter were women—explaining a cooking recipe and how to make the rations last longer. Politics was taboo. Who knew who might be an informer?

Then the bombs began to fall, and the antiaircraft guns opened up. It seemed incredible that anything would be left standing in Berlin. The cellar literally rocked.

"That was a close one," said one woman nervously, as the building shuddered, wondering whether such a remark was treason. Nobody commented on it. The mothers were occupied, soothing their crying children. Three hours later the all clear sounded, and a large section of Berlin no longer existed.

"And now, Renate," asked her father, "will you please repeat what you said when the air-raid interruption came?"

"Can't we leave it until tomorrow?" pleaded the mother. "It's late."

"I'd rather we talked about it now," answered Renate, "otherwise none of us will get any sleep. Just before the warning came, I told you that I am going to join a Youth Resistance Group."

"But you belong to the Hitler Youth Movement," said her mother.

"True, Mother, but you know, and Father knows, that I was forced to join it, or Father would have had to give a reason in writing for any refusal to do so. And that would have meant a concentration camp at least—to say nothing of Father losing his position."

"I don't understand you, Renate," said her puzzled father. "Aren't you satisfied with our Führer?"

"That's a question I wouldn't dare ask you, Father, for fear of the answer. But we, especially the youth of Germany, must do something, or the world will never know, when the war is over, that there were some Germans who hated all that Hitler stood for."

"Maybe," answered her father, "but that's no reason why you should join a Resistance Group! What positive action can you do against the Nazi Juggernaut?"

"I cannot go on as I'm doing now," answered Renate. "I'm sick of the false history I'm being taught. I've no faith in our totalitarian state, in this vast prison. If we, the young people, do not do something, then the civilized world will have the right to put all of us in the dock and condemn us."

"You suddenly see yourself as a Joan of Arc," said her father.

"Oh no, Father. I want to be just one of many. There are hundreds of us. . . ."

"We know," interrupted her mother, "but look what happens to them. Your father and I know the Huebner family well. We stayed with them in Hamburg. Their son, Helmut, was a wonderful boy. He, too, had ideas like you have. He was guillotined."

"And look what happened to the Scholls in Munich," said her father. "They rebelled and now brother and sister are dead."

"Oh, Father," pleaded Renate, "surely somebody in your circle must have told you what Bishop Galen of Münster preached in his cathedral, 'It may be that obedience to God and loyalty to conscience will cost you or me our lives, our freedom, or our home. But let us rather die than sin.' Let me show you the leaflet for which the Scholls died."

From her handbag Renate took out a sheet of paper.

"You must be mad to carry this around with you," said her mother. "Nothing could save you, or us, if this were found on you."

Instinctively she looked around the room, as though expecting one of the Gestapo to appear at any moment. Renate's father took the leaflet from her, and as he silently read it, Renate gave her own commentary for her mother's benefit.

"It tells how 330,000 men have been irresponsibly slaughtered at Stalingrad through the brilliant strategy of a mad Austrian corporal named Hitler."

"Hush, my dear," warned her mother, but Renate was in full spate.

"And whether we should sacrifice what is left of Germany's youth to satisfy this maniac."

From his coat pocket Renate's father took a lighter and set fire to the leaflet, flushing the ashes down the toilet.

"It would seem," he said very calmly, "that since you were given such a leaflet, you are obviously a member of a Youth Resistance Group."

"No, Father, I was given the leaflet because they trusted me. I wanted you both to know before I formally joined."

"I won't ask you for any details, but remember, Renate," he warned, "that there are spies everywhere. One false move, an unguarded word, and the SS and the Gestapo will pounce on you and inevitably on us. You are gambling with your life, and possibly with ours. Have you considered this?"

"Yes, Father."

"Then, if you have carefully considered all this and still want to join, there is nothing your mother or I can say."

"Thank you, Father. Thank you, Mother."

"And now," said her mother, "you had better go to bed, or you'll be unfit for school tomorrow."

Renate kissed her parents good night, and went to her room.

When she had gone, the parents looked at one another.

"She's your daughter, Manfred."

"And yours, Trude."

"Do you think she has any idea that we belong to Group K?"

"I don't think so, my dear, or she would have used it as a reason

for joining, but it was inevitable that she would join some Resistance
Group."

"We must do our best to watch over her."

It was her school friend, Grete, who sponsored Renate's membership of Group Y. Grete was the daughter of a doctor who held a
commission in the army, and who was principal surgeon in a military hospital in Berlin. Consequently, she wore her Hitler Youth
badge with great pride, except in the privacy of her own home.

This particular afternoon, when school was over, Grete led the
way to a bookshop close to the Kaiser Wilhelm Memorial Church.
The owner was poring over an old manuscript when the two girls
entered.

"Please, have you a good copy of Goethe's *Faust?*" asked Grete.

It was a question he had already been asked several times.

"You will find one in the back room," he answered, without
even looking up. He had recognized Grete's voice.

The two girls entered a small book-lined room, where a number
of girls and boys were browsing over books. To Renate's surprise,
two of the girls, Gertrud and Maria, and three of the boys, Fritz,
Kurt, and Hans, were old friends. They had hiked and camped together for many years. They had met as recently as the previous
week, but Renate had not suspected anything out of the ordinary.
No mention had been made of politics. She was introduced to Vera,
Elisabeth, Hanna, Wilhelm, Walter, and Dieter.

With the exception of one young man, each of them wore the
Hitler Youth badge. The young man, twenty years old, had one
arm and wore an army decoration. It was to this man, leader of the
Youth Group, that Grete introduced Renate.

"This is Renate B———."

The young man shook hands with Renate, and said "Carl."

"Please sit down, Renate. I would like to talk to you."

Carl then explained very seriously to Renate, just as her parents
had done, what joining a Resistance Group meant to each individual
member. A false move, a thoughtless word, could mean death to all
of them. Above all, to beware of anybody outside the group, and if
anybody asked questions, to deny any knowledge of the group.
Deny, deny, deny, always deny.

❋

Three days later (it was a Saturday) Renate set out on her first mission. It was to an art shop in the Uhland Strasse.

"Is the Professor in?" asked Renate on entering the shop.

"He's busy," answered a young girl assistant. "What do you want to see him about?"

"I've come about art lessons. He has been recommended to me as a very good teacher."

"Wait a moment."

The girl went to a door at the back of the shop and rapped a signal on it. The door opened and out came an elderly man, spectacles on his nose, brush in hand, and peered over his glasses at Renate.

"Good morning, miss. What can I do for you?"

"It's about lessons."

"Oh yes, I might be able to manage. Come this way," and the Professor led the way to a back room, where all the paraphernalia was set out for art lessons. He pointed to a desk on which was a half-finished crayon drawing, and said, "That is yours. Not bad for a first effort."

On the table was a drawing board, on which was pinned a sheet of paper, headed REICHSMARSHAL HERMANN GOERING, PATRON OF THE ARTS. Below was a list of famous paintings taken from world museums, known to be in the possession of Hermann Goering.

"A useful exercise for the future," said the elderly man, pointing to the board, "and also useful if any inquisitive people come nosing around. It looks good, doesn't it?" He gave a jolly little laugh. "As you are going to take lessons with me, you had better introduce yourself and tell me why you came today."

Renate, who had set out on her first mission with a great deal of trepidation, was surprised how calm and collected she was. The Professor certainly inspired her with confidence. She repeated word for word the message Carl had given her. A complete set of papers were needed urgently for a young woman who had fled from the Gestapo in Bremen. The Professor jotted down the details in his own code, and promised to work as quickly as was possible.

He saw Renate to the door, said he would always be glad to see her for her lesson, and asked her to take care of herself. He then went down by a hidden door to a little cellar, which was his workshop.

Renate walked on air. It was a fine day and she felt that she had accomplished something to thwart the Nazis, no matter how small. She may have helped a human being to escape from an irresponsible gang of thugs. Life had some meaning for her. She would see if Grete was home, and together they might go for a good long walk. Not that she would mention anything of her visit to the Professor.

"Trust no one," Carl had said, "not your father, or mother, or your best friend." Her reverie was roughly interrupted by a man walking alongside her and clutching her arm. Renate was terrified, but tried to control herself.

"Are you Renate B——?"

"Yes," stammered Renate.

The grip on her arm tightened.

"You must come with me," and he led her across the road to a dilapidated office, where he almost propelled her up a staircase to a room on the first floor. He knocked on the door, obviously a prearranged signal. A key was turned in the lock, and a stern, grim-faced woman opened the door. Renate was led into the barely furnished room. It contained three kitchen chairs, a desk, a camp bed, and, in a corner, a basin with a cold water tap.

"Sit down," said the man to Renate, pointing to a chair. He sat opposite to her, on the other side of the desk. The woman sat beside him.

"You are Renate B——?"

"Yes."

"Give me your handbag," said the woman. Renate handed it over. The woman opened it, and turned out the contents on the desk. She quickly examined them, and returned them to the bag.

"Nothing," she reported, and handed back the bag to Renate, who by now was bewildered and, despite the warm day, cold with fear.

"Keep calm, keep calm," she told herself.

"We have every reason to believe," said the man, "that you belong to a Youth Resistance Group."

"I don't know what you're talking about," replied Renate. "You can see by my badge that the only youth movement I belong to is the Hitler Youth."

"We know all about that," countered the man. "All you members of the Resistance Groups belong to the Hitler Youth as a blind. You cannot fool us that way. What is the name of your group?"

"I don't know what you're talking about," protested Renate.

"Where have you been this morning?" asked the woman.

"Nowhere," answered Renate. "It's a fine day and I thought I would go for a walk."

"Alone?"

"Yes, I enjoy walking alone."

"But we know that there was a reason for your walk."

Had one of the group turned traitor? This flashed through Renate's mind. Deny, deny, deny, hammered in her brain.

Renate smiled.

"The only reason for my walk is the fine weather."

"Your obstinate silence," said the woman, "may mean that this walk you evidently enjoyed so much will be the last one you will ever take. Except, perhaps, to the gallows. Let that sink into your mind."

The man turned to the woman.

"Which do you think? The police headquarters in Alexanderplatz or the Gestapo in the Prinz Albrechtstrasse?"

"I think," suggested the woman, "that this might be a case for the People's Court. The President Freisler is especially keen to try young people after the Scholl affair in Munich. We would, of course, reserve seats for her parents."

"But maybe as a first move it could be prison," suggested the man.

"Perhaps our young lady doesn't know the sort of welcome that awaits her," answered the grim-faced woman. "She doesn't know that she will walk through two lines of SS, who will be armed with whips and sticks."

"But that's only a preliminary," added the man. "Then there's the favorite SS method of eliciting information, smearing tar over the body and setting fire to it."

"Alternatively," said the woman, "we might suggest the rack, or the pulling out of the toenails. What do you think?"

"It depends on the young lady herself."

He turned to Renate. "Tell us the names of some of the people in your group, say, just six of them, and we can spare you this torture."

"Or even just the leader of the group," added the woman.

"I don't know what you're talking about," said Renate.

Her mouth and her throat were dry. She moistened her lips with the tip of her tongue.

Deny, deny, deny! A group is like a chain. It is only as strong as its weakest link. That's what Carl had said.

"So you definitely refuse to cooperate?" spat out the woman.

"There's nothing to cooperate about," said Renate. "I don't know why you've brought me here."

"You know that this may mean the concentration camp or a quick execution. It will break your parents' hearts. Oh yes, we know that you have very respectable parents. It may be the end for them too. So if you have any love for them, or any thoughts of them, tell us what we want to know. Speak!"

"I still don't know what you're talking about. There's nothing I can tell you."

Renate felt the color coming back to her cheeks. She was now resigned to her fate. She had had a short inglorious career, perhaps helping to save one life, but losing her own in doing so.

Then, suddenly, everything changed. The sun shone through the murky window, and transformed the grim-faced woman into a kindly matron. She rose and embraced Renate. There was quite a tremor in her sympathetic voice when she spoke.

"I'm sorry, Renate, that we gave you such a grueling, but we had to make sure that you are a suitable person to join the Resistance Group Y. You have come through the ordeal magnificently. You will be a credit to the group."

The man put out his hand which Renate took. She was now trembling.

"Please forgive me too," he said, "but we know that you appreciate that had you failed the ordeal, you would have been dropped. We cannot be too careful. We are gambling with many lives, young ones, and we want to win. And now"—he smiled—"let us adjourn to a café and celebrate our new friendship."

*

Grete needed food coupons. Things were becoming very scarce in Berlin, and rations were becoming smaller. The boast that Russia would be a vast granary for the Third Reich had been exploded. The German and Italian armies had been routed in North Africa, and the Allies had landed in Sicily. The armies needed more food. The civilians must suffer.

For two years, Grete had looked after an old couple who had been sheltered in the attic of her father's house. Their son had been one of the fiercest anti-Hitler members of the Reichstag. He was marked down for extermination, but he succeeded in escaping to Switzerland.

It was Grete's father who tipped off the old couple that they were on the Gestapo list, and offered them a home with his family, which they gratefully accepted. For two years now they had not dared to go into the street, and even now, when air raids were becoming more frequent, they dared not go into an air-raid shelter. False papers were no use to them. They could not be certain of anonymity. Somebody might recognize them, or in addition to the air raid, there might also be a raid by the Gestapo or the SS, and even false papers would almost certainly be ineffective in their case. They prayed that the house would escape a direct hit. It had been Grete who had acted as quartermaster, scrounging coupons from members of the group.

Just when Grete had almost despaired of getting more coupons, there came the most providential windfall. She and Renate were going home by tram, after a meeting of the group. The sirens screeched an air-raid warning. The tram stopped and emptied. Everybody ran to the nearest shelter. On their way to the shelter the two girls had to pass a grocery shop, which was open but deserted.

"Quick," said Grete, as she dived into the shop and scooped up from old cigar boxes handfuls of coupons, which she stuffed into her handbag. Renate did the same, and within a minute they had joined a crowd of people in the shelter.

"Don't have any guilt feelings about this, Renate," whispered Grete. "Taking anything from the Nazis is not stealing."

Fortunately the warning was a false alarm, not an uncommon occurrence, since the people in charge were becoming jittery. Now

Grete was happy. She was adept at swapping. With the coupons she had she could swap for milk or tobacco or vegetables, or smoked food and meat.

It was a gloomy meeting of the group in the church hall. Kurt had been arrested by the Gestapo, and was to be tried in the People's Court.

"But surely," argued some members of the group, "they can only send him to prison. They don't know that he belongs to a group." What was Kurt's crime? He was helping to put out fires after an air raid. "Fires like this will consume the Third Reich," he said as he doused the flames.

The concierge heard this and reported him. He was arrested, and sent for trial at the People's Court. Meanwhile he had been tortured and beaten, more as a matter of form than to discover anything.

Through her father, who tried to dissuade her from attending, Grete had obtained a pass for the trial in the People's Court.

The other members of the group were awaiting the return of Grete from the Court. When she came in, it was evident that the worst had happened. She tried to control herself to give a coherent account.

"I hardly recognized Kurt. They had beaten him mercilessly. To complete his humiliation they had taken away his suspenders, his belt, and his tie, so that he had to clutch his trousers to prevent them falling down. All this amused the President of the Court, the unspeakable Roland Freisler—may his soul burn in Hell—and the audience; for it was like being at a circus, or seeing, again enacted, the throwing of the Christians to the lions in Ancient Rome. 'It's better than the theater,' said a woman sitting next to me. There was one brave man sentenced to death before Kurt was brought in. He was accused of distributing subversive leaflets. When Freisler began to amuse the Court at the poor victim's expense, the man in the dock retorted, 'You must hurry up getting me hanged, Herr President, or you will be strung up before me.' Kurt's lawyer was hopeless. He pointed out that Kurt was still a schoolboy, and that he did not mean any harm. Also that his father was a soldier who had been awarded the Iron Cross. This infuriated Freisler all the more. The son should have known better. When sentence of death was pronounced, they dragged Kurt out and his mother collapsed. He saw me and tried to smile."

"Is there anything we can do?" asked several of the group.

"There's only one man who can save him," said Carl, "and that is Himmler, and none of us knows him."

"I've an idea," almost shrieked Grete. "Himmler's personal doctor is a friend of my father's," and she ran out of the hall. The rest of the group waited, in almost absolute silence. For the first time it was brought home to them how perilously they were gambling with their own lives and with those of other people. An hour passed. No news from Grete. Another thirty minutes, and Grete came in, tears streaming down her cheeks. Kurt had been hanged as soon as he was taken from the Court.

Hardest hit in the group by the murder of Kurt were Hans and Maria. They lived on the same street as Kurt and had been friends since childhood. On their visit to Kurt's parents, they were shown an "account" sent to them by the Gestapo for the murder of their son. It set out the amount the parents had to pay.

Fee for Death Penalty	Rm 280.30
Fee for Counsel for Defence	Rm 106.50
Charge for Maintenance in Prison	Rm 52.60
Cost for Carrying Out the Sentence	Rm 161.30
Postage	Rm 2.10
Total	Rm 602.80

Ways and means of raising this money were discussed at a meeting of the group, since Kurt's parents could not raise such a sum without selling part of their home. It was their leader, Carl, who suggested that the members of the group leave it to him.

No member knew that he was also a member of Group K, and nobody would have been more surprised than Renate and Grete had they known that their parents had paid the "account" between them.

To learn the truth the group had to listen to the BBC news bulletins. They moved from house to house and from cellar to cellar to do this, and fixed their radio sets so that the dial always pointed to a German station, in case they were caught unawares.

It was now what the group called the "Poster and Leaflet Season." It was easy enough to be lighthearted about it, but that was really to hide the fears that lay beneath the knowledge that possession of a leaflet, or being caught pasting up one, meant death.

These leaflets were duplicated on old machines, hidden in homes or cellars. Since machines or typewriters had to be registered so that the seller and buyer were known to the State, and since nearly every one had some peculiarity in its letters, it was indeed gambling with death to type a leaflet and to copy it.

Group Y were fortunate. They had acquired an old typewriter that had once belonged to an American firm which had been active in Berlin in prewar days.

They typed the news given by the BBC and headed the leaflets "THE TRUTH." Then would follow items like this:

"Do you know that our armies have been smashed on the Russian Front?

Do you know that millions of soldiers are being sacrificed by the mad Austrian corporal named Hitler, to satisfy his lust for power?

Do you know that his coconspirator Mussolini is finished? The Italian people have had enough of him.

SABOTAGE THE WAR EFFORT

ORGANIZE ARMED RESISTANCE"

Empty boxes of soap powders, empty tea and seed packages were filled with leaflets and circulated.

Members of the group even put them in stores, so that they could not fail to reach the women who went shopping and who were suffering, not only from the hardship of severe rationing, but also from the absence of their menfolk at the front.

It was the turn of Renate and Fritz to do some leaflet posting. The night would be dark, no moon, and they chose a part of Berlin that still looked like a normal city. In answer to Hitler's boast of erasing Britain's towns, the Royal Air Force and the United States Air Force had swept over Berlin like a giant tornado, turning parts of Berlin into acres of rubble, with here and there a piece of masonry standing like a jagged tooth.

Carl, dressed in his old army uniform—he could always claim that he was on the Reserve, even though he had only one arm—went with Renate and Fritz. It would avoid any suspicion if two young people were accompanied by an old soldier. He could always vouch for them if they were in a jam.

Renate put up her first poster on the wall of a post office. This seemed to give it Government sanction. They used a tube of glue, which took up little space in a pocket. They had scarcely walked away twenty paces when two SS men on motorcycles raced past. They did not stop. The three breathed a sigh of relief.

They next paid a visit to the blacked-out railway station where they pasted up leaflets on timetables, thus making sure that plenty of people would read them in the morning.

The next poster went up on the wall of a bakery. The customers tomorrow morning would have something to talk about. They had barely turned the corner when two policemen came toward them. Renate and Fritz drew back into a doorway and went into a lovers' clinch, while Carl tried to light a cigarette, shielding the flame with his hand, as best he could, as the two policemen came abreast of them.

"What's happening here?" asked one of the policemen.

"Nothing," laughed Carl. "I'm trying to light a cigarette and two lovers are enjoying themselves. It's more than I can do with one arm."

"Where did you lose it?" asked the second policeman. This was more interesting than a couple of young lovers, who sheepishly left the doorway and went on down the street.

"By the French Maginot Line."

"I had a brother there," said the policeman. "He's now in Paris—lucky devil."

"You can say that again," said Carl. "I wish they'd send me there. Ah, well, let's hope it's all over soon. So long. Heil Hitler!"

"Let's hope they don't see the poster on the bakery," said Carl, when he caught up with Fritz and Renate. "We'd better go into the back streets."

They dropped a batch of soap powder envelopes around a grocery store. They would be rushed for in the morning; and after a few more errands they made for home.

"I'm sorry we're finished," said Renate, who was quite exhilarated by the night's adventure.

"Don't get punch-drunk," warned Carl. "It's too dangerous for that. One slip, and it's the end."

Carl and Fritz saw Renate to her home. Her father had gone on business to Heidelberg, and her mother was waiting up for her although it was not very late.

"You look flushed, darling," said her mother.

"It's the night air," answered the radiant Renate.

"Let's leave it at that," said her mother. "Make yourself something hot before going to bed."

July 20, 1944. The group had been called to a special meeting in the bookshop. They had not been there for several weeks, and many guesses were made for the reason of this special call.

"Since the Allies landed in France in June," whispered Hans to Gertrud, "I have seen people take the Swastika out of their buttonholes. After the debacle in North Africa, this must be the beginning of the end."

The phone rang. Carl answered it.

"Is that the Classic Bookshop?"

"It is."

"You made inquiries about my private library."

"Yes, I did."

"I'm very sorry but it is *not* for sale. I repeat, *not* for sale."

"Are you sure? No chance of another decision?"

"No chance at all. Definitely *not* for sale."

A very despondent Carl put the receiver down. All the members of the group had heard the conversation, and could not make head or tail of it.

At this moment the proprietor of the shop entered with a special edition of a newspaper, which he handed to Carl, who spread it out on the table. An attempt had been made on Hitler's life in the "Wolf's Lair," his headquarters in East Prussia. It had failed.

"That's why this meeting was called," said Carl. "We were certain of success, and our group were given specific duties to perform. The phone call confirmed this news. And now I advise you all, indeed I command you all, to lie low and to do nothing for a time. The Gestapo will lay about them right and left. The innocent will suffer with the guilty. As you know, two hundred and fifty prisoners have been put to death in Plötzensee Prison to make room for new prisoners. So I plead with you to be careful." Carl looked at his watch. "Turn on the radio, Hans. Let's listen to the news."

The announcer confirmed the attempted assassination of the Führer, and that Hitler would speak to the nation.

"Lying low" was easier said than done, to members of the group. Following the abortive *coup d'état,* the Gestapo went berserk. Group K had infiltrated one of their members into the Gestapo, and consequently they were often tipped off about imminent arrests. These tips were sometimes passed on to Carl, who brought in some of his Group Y to help the marked people to escape.

This meant refuges for them. No two successive nights were spent in the same place. Nor could the young Resistance Group neglect those for whom they had cared. There were men and women who had not dared to go out into the street for four years. They needed to be fed. Coupons had to be found, and, above all, they needed to be given hope that, as the plotters of the July 20 *coup* put it, "We want to rehabilitate our honor, and thereby our reputation in the community of nations."

It was still essential to listen to the BBC news bulletins. How else was one to know that the Russian steamroller was annihilating the German Army, and that their onetime comrades, the Italian Army, were left to find their way across Europe on foot, since the proud German Army was using every vehicle to fall back and escape?

On the twentieth of August, 1944, General de Gaulle entered Paris, the city where Hitler had danced in triumph, assuring the world that the Nazi Third Reich would last a thousand years.

Somehow this news had to be told to as many people as possible, and Carl and his group had to forget the policy of "lying low," and they put out as many leaflets as they could.

They also went "rubber-stamping."

The art professor had made them good-size rubber stamps bearing the words "Listen to the Freedom Sender. Tune in to wave-length 1500 to learn the truth, and nothing but the truth."

Phone booths and billboards were the favorite places for the stamps.

They met in a Church Hall. The group knew that the pastor was sympathetic to their ideas and ideals but, ostensibly, it was as the Hitler Youth that he allowed the group to meet in the hall.

It was the twenty-first of October, 1944, and Carl gave the good news to his group that Belgrade had fallen to the Red Army.

He also introduced Ernst, an undergraduate of Heidelberg, who was on the run from the Gestapo. He was dodging his call-up.

A strange coincidence, thought Renate. My father is in Heidel-berg giving a series of lectures. I wonder what Ernst's subject is. But it was a strict rule not to ask questions. It was enough that Carl vouched for a person. Carl could have told Renate that it was her father who had persuaded Ernst to leave Heidelberg, with an intro-duction—verbal, of course—to Carl.

"We need to put our complete machinery in motion," said Carl. "You, Renate, will visit the Professor for a complete set of papers. We will decide on name, place of birth, etc. You, Grete, must . . ."

Just then the bell rang. It was the pastor's warning that strangers were at the door. Carl gave the order—"First Aid"—and, taking Ernst by the hand, he led him to a far corner, opened the door, gave him the key, and said, "Lock yourself in. You will be in the church. I will knock five times when I want you to come out."

Fritz was lying on the floor, one sleeve of his shirt was rolled up, and a first-aid box was prominently displayed. Gertrud was holding two splints.

The door was flung open and two black-uniformed SS men en-tered, followed by the pastor.

"Now, explain again, Gertrud," said Carl. "Oh, good evening, gentlemen—this is our First Aid Class . . . "

"Papers!" shouted one of the SS men.

The coats, bearing the Hitler Youth badge, had been neatly placed on the floor, with the badges prominent. Each member of the group went to his coat, the girls to their handbags and produced the necessary papers.

"They are loyal citizens of the Third Reich," murmured the pastor, "as you can see. Otherwise they would not be allowed to meet here."

The SS men were satisfied and shouted, "Carry on! Heil Hitler!" to which the group responded suitably. They departed, followed by the pastor. After a reasonable pause and three short sharp rings on the bell, Ernst rejoined the group, and the meeting continued.

Grete's family, her father, mother, and herself, were spending the evening at home quietly—that is, as quiet as a probable bombing raid allowed them to be.

There was an air of contentment too. They had just heard that day that Grete's brother was a prisoner of war in France, and that her sister, a nurse, was working in a hospital in Northern Italy, in a comparatively safe town.

"May I interrupt your reading, Father?" asked Grete.

Her father looked up and smiled.

"Tell me, Father," continued Grete, "if you were to examine a man for the army . . . "

"I don't examine men for the army," interrupted her father.

"I know that, Father. Not now. But you did once."

"That's true, I did one batch in my spare time in 1942, when they were short of doctors."

"Then tell me, Father, what would make a man unfit for the army?"

Grete's father laughed. "Since when are you so interested in my work?"

"Just curiosity," answered Grete.

"Well," said the father, "to satisfy your curiosity, a weak heart might be sufficient, or an illness of the kidneys, or blindness, or lung trouble, or one of a dozen afflictions."

"I suppose if a man had rheumatic fever as a child, it might leave him with a bad heart," suggested Grete, "and jaundice could affect his liver."

"Your diagnosis could be correct, Grete," laughed her father. "And now, to cut this long story short, what is the name of the man I was supposed to have examined in 1942 and to have rejected for the army?"

Grete flung her arms about her father and kissed him.

"Oh, Father, you are wonderful."

✳

"How was Heidelberg, Father?" asked Renate.

"Pretty much like any other city at the moment," answered her father. "Perhaps a little less apprehensive about being wiped out from the air."

"Did you by any chance meet an undergraduate named Ernst Busch?"

"I meet so many undergraduates in the course of my lectures. It would be impossible for me to remember the names of those introduced to me. Should I remember this Ernst Busch?"

"Not necessarily, Father," answered Renate. "Only now he is Heinz Fritsch. I met him the other day. He was rejected by the doctor for the army, and decided that there might be a better chance for a job in Berlin."

"So," said her father.

"I asked whether you know him because his subject at the university is Architecture, so he probably attended your lectures on 'Architecture in the Third Reich.' I wondered if he could be of any assistance to you, Father, in your work. All his papers and so on are in order."

"If it pleases you, Renate, I will certainly see him."

And so Heinz Fritsch was introduced into the household of Renate's parents, especially as every citizen with a spare room was asked to take people who had no home.

But Renate's first task was to take him to the all-powerful concierge who had a list of everybody who lived, or wanted to live, in the apartment house. Renate explained that Heinz Fritsch had been rejected for the army.

"Lucky devil," exclaimed the concierge.

He was to be her father's assistant and would be staying with them in their apartment.

"You couldn't be with nicer people," said the concierge.

"Thank you, Frau Schroeder, and we couldn't have a nicer concierge either."

For Christmas gifts, Renate's father decided to buy four second-hand bicycles.

"We may need them," he said.

JANUARY, 1945.

A meeting of the group in the Church Hall, had just miraculously escaped the bombers. The little bookshop was now a mound of rubble, as were many of their meeting places in Berlin. Houses were disintegrating.

The boast of Hitler that his secret weapon, the V-I (*Vergeltungswaffe*—Retribution weapon), would win the war for Germany, had proved an idle boast.

"I know that there are men hanging from lampposts and branded as cowards and deserters," said Carl, "but we must still go on urging the men and women in the Services to desert."

"I suggest," said Fritz, "that we all join the 'werewolves.' They may not take the girls, but if they give us a gun so that we can, as they proclaim, resist to the last moment, and we move nearer the front, we can do some real sabotage. It alleges to be a German Freedom movement, with its own courts to judge who is a traitor, and their battle cry is revenge and hatred for the enemy. Just as the Hitler Youth badge has stood us in good stead, so will membership of the werewolves."

"An excellent idea," agreed Carl, "and even though I've only one arm, they will take me and make a hero of me. And so I might persuade them to let us stay together as a unit. Don't worry, girls, I won't be far away from you."

Before they left the hall, they listened to the BBC. They now had a battery radio. The electricity of the city had become too capricious. The news was momentous. The Red Army had reached German soil in East Prussia and Silesia. The beginning of the end had really begun.

FEBRUARY, 1945

The group was doing yeoman work. The boys persuaded men to disregard Hitler's lunatic order to defend every city to the last man, and the girls were doing their best to find clothes for deserters, and to get them identity papers as discharged soldiers, or as unfit men. Most of them, like almost all the inhabitants of Berlin, were living in air-raid shelters.

The third of February was a day to remember. It was the biggest daylight raid on Berlin—by United States bombers—yet attempted by the Allies. The cellar in which members of the group were taking shelter literally shook.

"It is the end of the world," said one old woman during a momentary lull in the bombardment. Just then a man rushed into the cellar. How he had lived through the bombing, he himself could not tell, but he imparted one piece of news that sent a thrill through many of those in the cellar.

"The People's Court has been hit and is in flames," he said excitedly.

"Was it sitting?" asked Maria.

"Yes. The President Roland Freisler was just sentencing my nephew to death when the sirens went. The SS and Gestapo would not let me go into the cellar there. I ran out into the street and was at the other end, when the Court was hit. I ran all the way till I saw this shelter."

Nobody said a word. Nobody dared express an opinion. Somewhere in the crowd there could be an informer. Hours later, when the group met, they heard the news that during the air raid, a heavy beam in the cellar of the People's Court had fallen on Freisler's head and killed him instantly.

"Alas, years too late," murmured Maria.

For the next few weeks Dante's Inferno was child's play compared with Berlin. The people sensed that the city was dying.

In between the air raids they stood in line after line, getting rid of their ration coupons. They realized that soon they would be worthless, and that anything they could get for them was better than nothing.

April 13. Carl tuned into the BBC. The Red Army had occupied Vienna. The end was almost in sight. The group, acting as "werewolves," continued their sabotage—Walter and Max specializing in cable cutting.

More bombing and more bombing.

Would it never end?

Every day, in between raids, members of the group slipped home to make sure that all was well with their families.

"We have been waiting for you," said Renate's father. "We have decided to ride our bicycles to Magdeburg, to your aunt. Trains are no longer running and the city is cut off from the world. I would sooner that we are taken by the Allies than by the Soviet. They are more stable and less temperamental, and they have less cause for revenge. Refugees from Silesia are pouring in. We are leaving immediately."

"I'm sorry, Father, I cannot go. I cannot leave the group."

"But what can you do?" pleaded her mother. "It is all over. There is no light, no gas, no water—every drop is from street hydrants—no mail. We are cut off from the world."

"There are still deserters to look after," countered Renate, "still men and women on the run from the Gestapo, still motherless children. Grete and I are looking after four of them. I would feel like a rat if I left my comrades now. Please go without me. Give my bicycle to Frau Schroeder, our concierge."

"Do you know what people are giving for a bicycle?" asked her mother. "They are giving everything they possess."

"I know, Mother, but I must stay and see this through."

News and rumors. Everybody had a different story to tell. Was it true that the Allies and the Red Army had now met at Torgau?

With an old soldier's cunning, Carl borrowed a jeep from the werewolf headquarters, and with Wilhelm and Dieter—the three of them armed with submachine guns—set off on a reconnaissance, to see what harm they could do to Hitler's last-ditch stand.

They halted on the edge of a forest. Under Carl's guidance they took cover. Somebody was moving toward them through the wood. Friend or enemy? Carl whispered instructions what to do in either case.

With slow, measured steps, a Russian sergeant came out of the wood and cautiously approached the jeep. He was obviously leading a patrol and had got some way ahead of them. Within a minute, the three members of the group had disarmed the Russian, bundled him into the jeep, and raced back to their cellar in Berlin.

It was all so sudden that the Russian hardly realized what had happened to him, particularly when Carl stripped him of his tunic and cap, and kept repeating *Tovaritch,* the only Russian word he knew. The Russian spoke no German and was very puzzled why he had not been shot, and why Carl kept on assuring him that he was a *Tovaritch*.

"This is a godsend," said Carl. "It's the best day's work we've done for months."

They brought the sergeant into the crowded cellar, and put him into a corner. Nobody took the slightest interest and even when Carl asked if anybody present could speak Russian, few even looked up from what they were doing.

"I can speak Russian," piped up a little old man, sitting in the opposite corner.

"Please come over here," said Carl.

The old man zigzagged his way across the crowded cellar.

"Tell this Russian," whispered Carl—because even now there might be an informer about—"that we are his friends, that there are many Germans who hate Hitler just as he does, and that we want him to stay with us until it is all over. He is safe here, but we don't want any funny business. Also, ask him his name."

The old man translated this to the Russian, who brightened visibly. The Russian said that he trusted them, that he would stay with them, and that there would be no funny business. His name was Sergei. He shook hands warmly with the old man and then with Carl.

"Tell me," said Carl to the old man, "I haven't seen you down here before. You're welcome, of course . . ."

The old man smiled.

"Those are strange words," he said. "Aren't you going to say 'Papers!' like they all do?"

"Of course, papers are useful," began Carl. Then the old man told his story in staccato sentences.

"Three and a half years in a cellar, hidden by a kindly Christian family who didn't even know me. You see, I had committed the greatest crime in Hitler's eyes. I was born a Jew. The cellar was beneath their dress shop, and they lived above the shop. For three and a half years, the two daughters, Anneliese, now fifteen, and Sophie, fourteen, brought me food and drink every day. They gave me the news, they played chess with me, they comforted me. For three and a half years, the family of four risked their lives, especially the young ones, to feed an old Jew they didn't know.

"Then a few weeks ago I awoke early one morning and said to myself, 'I must see the sky again and the sun, just once more.' I had not seen them for three and a half years. So I crept up the stairs and let myself out of the house. I was almost delirious. I could not believe that I was alive. Slowly, very slowly, I walked to the Tiergarten. I looked up to the sky and I said a prayer to God. Then my light was blotted out. In front of me stood a policeman, who barked the word 'Papers!' I feigned loss of memory. He stopped a motorist, and made him drive us to the Gestapo prison in the Prinz Albrechtstrasse, where I was thrown into a cell with about twenty other people.

"But God was good. He had heard my prayer. Soon the American bombers came over and hit the prison. In front of us was a big hole in the wall. We all walked through it and I returned to my cellar. Oh, were they happy to see me!

"Yesterday there was another raid. Our house was hit. My good, kind friends were killed—peace be upon their souls—and I, poor devil, was left alive. Why couldn't it have been the other way round?"

"Don't worry, Grandfather, your troubles will soon be over."

The old man laughed.

"That's funny, I am a grandfather. But they took my children and my grandchildren away from me four years ago. Only those two angels, Anneliese and Sophie, called me grandfather," and tears streamed down the old, wrinkled face. "A little water, please," he murmured.

"Some water, Max, please," called Carl.

"I am just going for some," said Max, taking up two buckets. "I won't be long—the hydrant's only around the corner."

Old men, old women, children, were lining up at the hydrant. Every kind of utensil that could hold water was being used. Every time a plane flew over, even a German plane, the people would fall flat on the ground.

Eventually it was Max's turn. He filled the buckets and as he turned the corner, a shell exploded in the street. A fragment of the shell hit him and killed him instantly. Ten minutes later, Renate went in search of him. She found him, still gripping the handles of the overturned buckets.

✼

The Russians were now shelling the city in earnest. Tanks were on the outskirts. The tunic and hat had been restored to Sergei, and nobody in the cellar took the slightest notice of him.

Then on the last day of April, 1945, three armed Russian soldiers triumphantly and vengefully rushed into the cellar, but a word of command from Sergei who stood there, submachine gun at the ready, rooted them where they stood. Another stream in Russian and out went the three soldiers as quickly as they had come in.

"Tell Carl," said Sergei to the old man, "that I will stand on guard outside until my comrades settle in the city. Nobody will harm anybody here."

MAY DAY, 1945.

People are running through Berlin, shouting that Hitler committed suicide yesterday, in his bunker. The news bulletins of the BBC confirm this. He died yesterday.

On the second of May, Berlin capitulated.

Carl led his Resistance Group out of the cellar. The old man went with them. They looked at a prostrate and dead city.

"Only our prophet Jeremiah could describe this, as he did the fall of Jerusalem," said the old Jew.

> How doth the city sit solitary, that was full of people!
> How is she become as a widow!
> She that was great among the nations,
> And princess among the provinces,
> How is she become tributary!

Then he turned to the group, and, as a prophet himself, he said, "If Germany is ever to come alive, you, the young people, must breathe life into it again. You will be the Children of the Light."

As the old man turned away to continue his solitary journey into the future, he was heard to murmur, "Not every German is a Nazi."

12359